Exploring Medical Ethics

Exploring
Medical Ethics

BY HENLEE H. BARNETTE

Mercer University
Press

All books published by Mercer University Press are produced
on acid-free paper which exceeds the minimum standards set by the
National Historical Publications and Records Commission.

Library of Congress Cataloging in Publication Data
Barnette, Henlee H.
    Exploring medical ethics.

    Bibliography: p. 149.
    Includes index.
    1. Medical ethics.   I. Title.   [DNLM:
1. Ethics, Medical—Case studies.   2. Religion—Case studies. W 50 B261e]
R724.B32   174'.2   82-2116
ISBN 0-86554-031-4   AACR2

Table of Contents

Dedication

To my colleagues on the medical staff of the University of Louisville School of Medicine with whom I have found a genuine koinonia.

One of the essential qualities of the clinician is interest in humanity, for the secret of the care of the patient is in caring for the patient.

Francis Peabody, M.D.

Foreword

The book you are about to read is unique among treatises on medical ethics. Professor Barnette has taken seriously three challenges that medical students and physicians level at those who presume to speak and write on medical ethics. The first of these criticisms is the "esoteric" way in which the subject is approached. Medical students say that the cases used by writers lack a genuine "everydayness"; they verge on science fiction. Henlee Barnette has worked for five years alongside medical students and resident physicians in case conferences about everyday, frequently occurring issues and cases. He writes from the "everydayness" context.

The second criticism is that the authors and writers do not get in the trenches with physicians in the grimy battle against disease, despair, and death. Professor Barnette writes from within the trenches where he has served as a highly esteemed colleague among physicians, nurses, psychologists, social workers, and pastoral counselors. When he writes about suicide he does so at the same time he seeks to bring meaning and reason for living to patients who are threatening suicide, who have attempted suicide, or to the family of a person who has completed a suicide. Each chapter in this book is about a problem presented often to Henlee Barnette by patients and/or staff persons in an inner city university medical center.

The third criticism of the medical community is their objection to making a "required course" or separate department of medical ethics. Professor Barnette perceives medicine as a whole as an intrinsically ethical enterprise. This enterprise cannot be relegated to one department or course. It is the responsibility of every department and best permeates the whole curriculum.

However, indispensable and basic information is needed by physicians, students of all kinds, and patients in a brief, readable, curiosity-arousing volume. In concise Anglo-Saxon words meaningful to all these readers, Professor Barnette has plumbed the depths of enquiry into medical issues of ethical importance. He uses the case method of enquiry. He discusses subjects not mentioned in other books on medical ethics, such as humor as a therapeutic tool.

This book will serve for years to come as a handbook and textbook for the student in his or her formation of a professional life—medical students, nursing students, theological students, social work students, and others. Patients and their families will find light and understanding in the difficult dilemmas of illness in the family.

The ultimate concerns of devout lovers of God and neighbor in the clutch of human pain are both illumined and humbly served in the mature wisdom of this exploration of medical ethics.

Wayne E. Oates, Th.D.
Professor of Psychiatry and Behavioral Sciences
Director, Program in Ethics and Pastoral Counseling
Department of Psychiatry and Behavioral Sciences
University of Louisville School of Medicine
Louisville, Kentucky

Acknowledgements

I must begin by acknowledging my indebtedness to Wayne E. Oates, Th.D., Professor in the Department of Psychiatry and Behavioral Sciences in the University of Louisville School of Medicine, who suggested that I do a book on the moral issues encountered routinely by medical personnel. The encouragement, helpful suggestions, and insights freely offered by Dr. Oates reflect the constancy of his friendship for over forty years.

To John Schwab, M.D., Chairman and Professor in the Department of Psychiatry and Behavioral Sciences, who warmly welcomed me to the Department as Clinical Professor and has been a constant source of intellectual stimulation and support, I am deeply grateful.

Also, I am grateful to other colleagues on the staff of the University of Louisville School of Medicine who read the manuscript as a whole or in part, suggesting improvements in content: Nancy Flowers, M.D., Chief of Cardiology; Wolfgang Kuhn, M.D., Associate Director of the Psychiatric Consultation-Liaison Program; Herbert Wagemaker, M.D., Director of Psychiatric Services; James D. McNeely, M.D., Medical Director of Norton Psychiatric Services; Sheldon Chase, M.D., Associate Clinical

Director of Norton Psychiatric Clinic; and Curtis Barrett, Ph.D., Director of Psychological Services and Clinical Psychologist. Of course, I am ultimately responsible for any errors that may appear in this volume.

In addition I am beholden to staff members of the medical complex where I work; Jenni Khaliel, Research Assistant in the Department of Psychiatry; Holly Buchanan, Librarian, Norton-Kosair Children's Hospitals; Jackie Wilhelm, Office Manager, Norton Psychiatric Clinic; the psychologists, nurses, art therapists, and aides of the Clinic; and Mrs. Hal Griffin, who typed the initial and final copy of the manuscript with great patience and skill. Also, Paul Debusman, Ph.D., Reference and Serials Librarian at Southern Baptist Theological Seminary, helped in the research of some of the theological materials.

Most of all I am indebted to my wife, Helen, who patiently read and reread the manuscript, suggesting needed changes in style and logical sequence. Her faith in the importance of this endeavor enabled me to stay with the task.

Henlee H. Barnette
University of Louisville
School of Medicine

Introduction

Medical personnel are constantly engaged in critical ethical decision making. Their decisions are critical because they relate to the health and happiness of persons. Theirs is a praxis profession, oriented to the more practical questions as to what should be done, often immediately, in particular concrete cases. Physicians must make technical decisions which are at the same time moral decisions because they have to do with the total person. The practice of medicine is an art for it is related to human values. As Eliot Friedson puts it, "Medicine is a moral enterprise."[1]

Ethical Dilemmas and Decisions in Medicine

As in the case of every profession, the physician finds few easy answers to moral issues related to his work. With the emergence of new biomedical technologies, ethical issues for the whole health care system

---

[1]Eliot Friedson, *Profession of Medicine: A Study of the Sociology of Applied Knowledge* (New York: Dodd, Mead, and Co., 1970), p. 208.

have become increasingly ambiguous and complicated. Current ethical dilemmas in biomedicine include such issues as technologies that prolong life of the terminally ill, genetic engineering, biomedical reproduction, behavior control, human medical experimentation, and human parts transplantation. Traditional codes of morals in medicine provide little specific guidance for such problems.

Numerous volumes have been written recently about medical ethics. Almost all of these are written from the philosophical perspective.[2] Few are written specifically from a theological perspective. Yet there is a growing interest on the part of Jewish and Christian theologians and ethicists in biomedical ethical problems.[3]

Is there any value in a theological approach structured largely according to a theological conception of the subject matter? I think that there is a need for such an approach where there is an integration of particular knowledge which different disciplines bring to the issues of biomedicine. An interdisciplinary approach involving *inter alia* philosophy, social sciences, science, psychology, law, theology, and ethics is the only way to arrive at a holistic (from the Greek *holos*, whole, entire, complete) view of the patients' problems and needs.

There are physicians who resent any "moral intervention" from *outside* of their profession. Ian Thompson, M.D., of Edinburgh, Scotland, argues that the personal moral responsibility of the doctors in making difficult moral decisions in clinical practice makes moral intervention from church or state, lay groups, or commercial interests "both irrelevant and impertinent."[4] He goes on to say that practical research in medical ethics must begin with physicians, nurses and patients, and, if moral theory is to be brought in, it is only when the peculiar issues surrounding *this* patient in *this* situation have been clarified.[5] Thompson concludes, however, that if the moral philosophers are "a part of a clinical team" and

---

[2]See the following basic ones: Samuel Gorovitch, et al., *Moral Problems in Medicine* (Englewood Cliffs, NJ: Prentice-Hall, 1976); Stanley J. Reiser, et al., eds., *Ethics in Medicine* (Cambridge, MA: The MIT Press, 1977).

[3]See James Gustafson, *The Contributions of Theology to Medical Ethics* (Milwaukee: Marquette University Theology Department, 1975); James B. Nelson, *Human Medicine: Ethical Perspectives on New Medical Issues* (Minneapolis: Augsburg, 1973); I. Jakobovits, *Jewish Medical Ethics* (New York: Block Publishing Co., 1959).

[4]"The Implications of Medical Ethics," *Journal of Medical Ethics* 2 (1976): 14.

[5]"The Role of the Philosopher in the Medical Team," *Journal of Medical Ethics* 3:1 (March 1977): 34.

will "work alongside their medical colleagues" and share some of their "practical dilemmas and often painful responsibilities," he will heartily approve the role of the moral philosopher in medical decisions.[6]

In America the ever-increasing number of moral dilemmas stemming from technological advances in medicine has made the ethicist a welcome colleague on many medical staffs. For example, a professor of philosophy and a medical doctor coteach a course in medical ethics at the University of Louisville School of Medicine, Louisville, Kentucky and also serve as ethics consultants for the school. In the department of psychiatry of this same school there is a professor who serves as Director of the Ethics and Pastoral Care Program.

Beyond and inseparable from the moral dimension of the person is the spiritual side which the physician cannot afford to ignore. It is commonplace now for chaplains to serve in the various kinds of health care institutions. Aware that a religious problem such as the loss of faith may impede the patient's progress toward wellness, physicians welcome pastoral care for such patients.

This study deals with human medical problems in the light of theological ethics in the Judeo-Christian tradition. The theological dimension is an essential component of a multidisciplinary approach to moral issues.

Technological advances in biomedicine demand the development of a comprehensive ethics. A set of ethical guidelines must be formulated to replace the traditional individualistic approach to moral decision making in health care delivery.

This study aims to present an approach to some of the ethical issues in medicine from the point of view of theological ethics. People are religious. Hence, the theological dimension which is essential to a multidisciplinary approach to moral issues is included in this volume.

Another feature which I hope this book can provide is some additional insight in dealing with issues often neglected in medical texts such as guilt, loneliness, elective death, and humor as a therapeutic tool.

Case Method Inquiry

The case method is an important tool of research in medical ethics, and will be employed in this study. Methodology has to do with the way in which research and the organization of materials are structured around a

---

[6]Ibid., pp. 34-35.

unifying principle or principles. The case method is not new by any means. For centuries it has been used in the study and practice of law. For over half a century it has been used at the Harvard Business School.[7] Even more recently, churches and seminaries are becoming aware of the case method to deal with actual moral and practical problems.[8]

Medicine, even more than law or business, is case oriented. A recent volume brings together more than one hundred studies which guide the student to an awareness and understanding of the moral dilemmas arising out of the everyday practice of modern medicine.[9]

Medical ethics simply cannot be done from the ivory towers of academe. Learning theory in the first years of medical studies is essential. But you must eventually start with the patient in a clinical situation. What will you tell a patient who is dying? What action will you take about keeping alive a terminally ill comatose patient? Will you perform surgery on a newborn baby with Downs Syndrome or respirate a badly-malformed one? What will you advise a woman who has discovered through the technique of amniocentesis that she is carrying a hemophiliac son or a Downs Syndrome? In the area of confidentiality would you report an epileptic pilot of a plane or motorist to the safety authorities? Will you report cases of child abuse to authorities? These and hundreds of other ethical issues challenge the physician in his day-to-day practice.

What is the case method? A case is an account of an actual problem or situation which has been experienced by an individual or a group. Instead of theoretical rules the case method uses descriptions of specific medical situations.

The case study approach has numerous values as well as limitations.[10] On the positive side the case study:

• has the appeal of a human interest story

• puts the student in touch with primary clinical data and is the closest thing to what Anton Boisen called "the living documents"

---

[7]Malcolm P. McNair, ed., *The Case Method at the Harvard Business School* (New York: McGraw-Hill Book Co., 1954).

[8]See Keith R. Bridston, ed., et al., *Case Book on Church and Society* (Nashville: Abingdon Press, 1974); and Wesner Fallow, *The Case Method in Pastoral and Lay Education* (Philadelphia: The Westminster Press, 1963).

[9]Robert M. Veatch, *Case Studies in Medical Ethics* (Cambridge: Harvard University Press, 1977).

[10]See Powell Niland, "The Values and Limitations of the Case Method," in McNair, *The Case Method*, pp. 87-92.

- brings theory and practice together
- allows the student to learn how to construct logical ways to deal with issues in medicine (he or she learns to break down problems, analyze them, and to make strategic decisions based on factual data)
- allows the student to become a participator rather than a spectator and consequently more apt to be stimulated intellectually and emotionally
- allows the student to learn to make decisions within time limitations (this is a primary factor for the physician who is often forced to make decisions within minutes to save a patient's life).

On the negative side, the case method has certain disadvantages:

- There is the temptation to force a positive solution, to take action where it may not be justified. For example, there may be an unwillingness *not* to operate on a patient whose cancer is so metastasized that there is really no hope of living.
- Then there is the danger that the case under study may oversimplify the medical issue. The case itself is a limited description of the medical situation and important factors may be left out. The case method may ignore statistical data of relevant value for the understanding of isolated examples. The case method cannot synthesize the whole medical situation.
- Finally, the case method is not infallible because it is the work of fallible human beings. In the collection of case materials there may be errors of omission and commission.

The case method is not a perfect method, but its advantages outweigh its disadvantages. On balance it is the most realistic method of developing skills in dealing with issues arising from biomedical technologies as well as the daily routine problems in the practice of medicine.

On how to read a case, the following suggestions appear to be pertinent:

- Read it carefully and critically.
- Ask, what is happening?
- Try to discover if there is more than one way to solve the problem.
- Report the facts as accurately and objectively and comprehensively as possible. Acceptable cases are built on facticity, not fiction.
- Protect the patient and yourself by using pseudonyms.

Purpose and Preview
This study is a concise treatment of theological ethics in medicine for

physicians, medical students, nurses, and clergymen who minister to the sick. It is a simply written but clinically informed handbook on medical ethics. It seeks to integrate special knowledge that different disciplines bring to biomedicine. These disciplines include philosophy, ethics, social sciences, sciences, and theology.

This study includes an overview of medical ethics, a suggested model for moral decision making in medicine, patient-physician relations, loneliness and its medical consequences, care of the guilt-laden patient, understanding the homosexual, communicating with cancer patients, suicide, death and dying, and the healing power of humor. Better research and health care can result from theological reflection on medical problems. (The chapters which follow, therefore, are designed to facilitate theological reflection on selected moral and theological issues in medicine.)

CHAPTER 1

Medical Ethics:
An Overview

George Bernard Shaw once declared: "An Englishman thinks he
is moral when he is only uncomfortable."[1] This pointed observation
captures the ambiguity of contemporary medical ethics.

This chapter will deal with basic terminology or definitions, the
major medical codes from the Hippocratic oath to the code of the
American Medical Association, and the development of medical morality
from etiquette to ethics as a discipline.

Basic Terminology

Medical ethics is sometimes identified with bioethics, but the latter
appears to be a more inclusive term. Derived from the Greek *bios* (life)
and *ethike* (ethics), the term bioethics was first used in 1971.[2] Bioethics

[1]George Bernard Shaw, *Man and Superman*, in *Collected Plays With Their Prefaces*
(New York: Dodd, Mead, and Co., 1975), 2:649.
[2]Van Rensselaer Potter, *Bioethics* (Englewood Cliffs, NJ: Prentice-Hall, 1971).

has been defined as "the systematic study of human conduct in the area of the life sciences and health care, insofar as this conduct is examined in the light of moral values and principles."[3]

Biomedical ethics is primarily concerned with medical research, technologies, and policies stemming from biomedicine. It tends to focus upon new discoveries such as biomedical reproduction, genetic engineering, human organ transplants, and human experimentation.[4]

Medical ethics is usually defined in general terms such as the following: "A system of principles governing medical conduct. It deals with the relationship of a physician to the patient, the patient's family, his fellow physicians, and society at large."[5] Generally, definitions of medical ethics are humanistic and grounded in reason. So S. J. Reiser, and others, state that "medical ethics is fundamentally grounded in moral principles and standards of reason and are a part of ethics generally, and in the accumulative wisdom of experience of medical knowledge and practice."[6]

A few writers on medical ethics work from Judeo-Christian presuppositions. Paul Ramsey of Princeton University holds that medical ethics "is consonant with the ethics of the wider human community. The former is . . . only a particular case of the latter; . . . canons of loyalty to patients or to joint adventures in medical research are simply particular manifestations of canons of loyalty of person to person generally."[7]

Some scholars see medical ethics as a species of the genus *ethics*.[8] H. R. Niebuhr, late professor of Christian ethics at Yale Divinity School, held that ethics is *one* and that Christian ethics is a species of ethics.[9] Arthur Dych, Harvard professor, thinks of medical ethics as a species of

[3]Warren T. Reich, ed., *Encyclopedia of Bioethics* (New York: The Free Press, 1978), p. xix.

[4]Kenneth Vaux, *Biomedical Ethics: Morality for the New Medicine* (New York: Harper and Row, 1974).

[5]Clayton L. Thomas, ed., *Taber's Cyclopedia Medical Dictionary* (Philadelphia: F. A. Davis Co., 1970), p. E-64.

[6]S. J. Reiser, et al., *Ethics in Medicine* (Cambridge, MA: MIT Press, 1977), p. 2.

[7]Paul Ramsey, *The Patient as a Person* (New Haven: Yale University Press, 1970), p. xii.

[8]Ibid.

[9]H. R. Niebuhr, *The Responsible Self* (New York: Harper and Row, 1936), p. 150.

ethics and that it "raises questions and employs methods systematically pursued and analyzed by ethics as a discipline."[10]

Medical Codes

Ethical guidelines for the practice of medicine are rooted in the Hippocratic corpus and its modifications through the centuries. Hippocrates, author of much of the corpus, was born on a Greek island about 460 B.C. He was a physician whose influence lives on through the code named for him. In the original code the physician swears—to the pagan gods of health and healing—to abide by the laws of the code. Among other things, the doctor swears: to *primum non nocere* (first, to do no harm), to perform no abortions, and not to practice euthanasia. (See Appendix A-1.)

Variant forms of the Hippocratic oath have appeared through centuries.[11] The oath was modified so that Christians could take it. Swearing by Apollo Physician, by Aesculapius, by Hygeia, by Panacea, and by all gods and goddesses was replaced by God the Father and the Lord Jesus Christ. With reference to not performing abortions, "by a pessary" in the original oath was replaced by "by any means." Unintentional harm to the patient is just as forbidden as intentional harm, so *criminal negligence* was entered for the first time in the medical code.[12]

Jewish medical ethics has been strongly influenced by the Prayer of Moses Maimonides written by Marcus Herz, a German physician, in the twelfth century. (See Appendix A-2.) A daily prayer before visiting patients, it recognizes God as the source of all healing and health. The highest motive for the practice of medicine is that of service. Love for mankind, not profit, ambition, admiration, or renown, is the motivation for being a physician. All social classes are to be readily served, including both enemy and friend. The true physician has a sense of divine calling to watch over the life and death of God's creatures.[13]

---

[10]Arthur Dych, *On Human Care: An Introduction to Ethics* (Nashville: Abingdon Press, 1977), pp. 25-26.

[11]See June Goodfield, "Reflections of the Hippocratic Oaths," in *The Hastings Center Studies* 1:2 (Hastings-on-Hudson, New York: Institute of Society, Ethics and Life Sciences, 1973): 79-92; and W. H. S. Jones, *The Doctor's Oath: An Essay on the History of Medicine* (Cambridge University Press, 1924).

[12]Jones, *The Doctor's Oath*, pp. 23-25.

[13]M. B. Etziony, *The Physician's Creed* (Springfield, IL: Charles C. Thomas, 1973), pp. 29-31.

The American Medical Association adopted an ethical code in 1847. This code was revised in 1903, 1912, 1947, 1955, and 1980. The introduction to the original code declares that medical ethics must rest on religion and morality. The code stresses duties of physicians to their patients and obligations of patients to their doctors, duties of physicians to one another and to the profession at large, duties to the public and duties of the public to physicians.[14]

The 1955 code of the American Medical Association deals with subjects such as consultation, scientific competence, professional courtesy, solicitation of patients, fees, conditions of practice, and confidentiality. It is a more secularized code from which specifically religious references as well as any reference to "Christian ethics" have been removed.

In 1957 the American Medical Association adopted "Principles of Medical Ethics." The preamble to this statement points out that these principles are intended to aid the physicians in maintaining a high level of ethical conduct. In 1980 the 1957 code of the American Medical Association was revised as follows:

AMA Principles of Medical Ethics

Preamble: The medical profession has long subscribed to a body of ethical statements developed primarily for the benefit of the patient. As a member of this profession, a physician must recognize responsibility not only to patients, but also to society, to other health professionals, and to self. The following Principles adopted by the American Medical Association are not laws, but standards of conduct which define the essentials of honorable behavior for the physician.

I.   A physician shall be dedicated to providing competent medical service with compassion and respect for human dignity.

II.   A physician shall deal honestly with patients and colleagues, and strive to expose those physicians deficient in character or competence, or who engage in fraud or deception.

III. A physician shall respect the law and also recognize a responsibility to seek changes in those requirements which are contrary to the best interests of the patient.

---

[14]"American Medical Association First Code of Medical Ethics" in *Ethics in Medicine,* Stanley S. Reiser, et al, eds. (Cambridge, MA: MIT Press, 1977), pp. 26-34.

IV.   A physician shall respect the rights of patients, of colleagues, and of other health professionals, and shall safeguard patient confidences within the constraints of the law.

V.   A physician shall continue to study, apply and advance scientific knowledge, make relevant information available to patients, colleagues, and the public, obtain consultation, and use the talents of other health professionals when indicated.

VI.   A physician shall, in the provision of appropriate patient care, except in emergencies, be free to choose whom to serve, with whom to associate, and the environment in which to provide medical services.

VII.   A physician shall recognize a responsibility to participate in activities contributing to an improved community.

These new principles represent radical changes in medical ethics and the changes were due to pressure from the Federal Trade Commission. Among the reasons for revision were (1) AMA's prohibition against doctors' advertising in order to elicit patients; (2) condemnation of chiropractic because it allegedly has no scientific basis; and (3) the breaking of confidentiality to benefit the patient. Traditionally, doctors have practiced therapeutic deception to protect some terminally ill patients from the trauma of bad news. Now they are under moral obligation to tell patients the truth.

The World Medical Association adopted The Declaration of Geneva in 1948 and the International Code of Medical Ethics was approved by the WMA in 1949. These codes represent the extension of a common body of medical ethics to the international level. They stress the service motive, fair fees, the preservation of human life, complete loyalty to the patient, and necessary treatment in emergency unless the doctor is assured that it can and will be given by others.

A set of Ethical and Religious Directives for Catholic Hospitals was published in 1949. The 1971 version was approved as a national code by the National Conference of Catholic Bishops. General directives deal with such issues as informed consent, confidentiality, and abortion. Among other things the section on Procedures Involving Organs and Functions forbids sterilization as a means of contraception. And under the category of "Other Procedures," euthanasia ("mercy killing") in all forms is forbidden. (See Appendix A-3.)

Medical Morality: From Etiquette to Ethics

The heritage of Hippocrates has evolved into numerous codes and collections of medical moral principles, rules, and maxims. In the process, medical morality has developed from the status of etiquette to that of ethics. Etiquette is a set of conventional rules that reflect conduct in polite society. Ethics is that discipline which seeks to articulate the ground, goal, and guidelines of right character and conduct in the light of reason, and, in religious terms, in the light of reason and revelation.

For centuries physicians and the public did not see any significant difference between medical etiquette and ethics. Confusion between the two persists even today.[15] Until the nineteenth century, codes of medical ethics focused primarily upon interpersonal relations between doctors and patients and other doctors. But even these were "the doctrines of morality or social manners."

John Gregory, professor of medicine at the University of Edinburgh, published, in 1772, his *Lectures on the Duties and Qualifications of a Physician*. According to L. L. King, this work laid the foundation for a formal code of ethics for the medical profession.[16] Gregory sharpened the definitions of the duties and responsibilities of the physician. Also he accented the virtues and the "gentlemanly dignity" of the physician.

An English physician, Thomas Percival, published a volume in 1803 entitled *Medical Ethics*. As did his predecessor, Gregory, Percival stressed the dignity and conduct of the doctor as essential to the behavior of a gentleman. Hence, his work was a treatise on the "gentleman physician," or a virtuous man as connoted by the term "gentleman" in the eighteenth century. Percival dealt with the relation of the physician to hospitals and medical charities, professional conduct in private and general practice, apothecaries, and legal matters. The faculty of physicians related to the hospital were provided guidelines for conduct, from bedside manners to rendering charity. In connection with the latter, Percival suggested that clergymen who experience the *res angusta domi* (meager circumstances at

---

[15]Chauncey D. Leake, "Theories of Ethics and Medical Practice," *The Journal of the American Medical Association* 208 (5 May 1969): 842.

[16]"Development of Medical Ethics," *The New England Journal of Medicine* 258 (6 March 1958): 480.

home) should be visited gratuitously by the faculty, but that those ministers who have money should pay for medical services.[17]

Percival's *Medical Ethics* has had considerable influence on the development of American medical ethics and practice. The influence of Percival is reflected in the first code of the American Medical Association of 1847 as well as in the 1957 edition. But the American emphasis has been on maxims rather than gentlemanly manners, and on rules rather than virtues. Hence there has been the enforcement of specific rules in the practice of medicine in America during the nineteenth and mid-twentieth centuries.

Medical Ethics in America

There is now a "new epoch" in medicine and medical morality in America. The new technologies in biomedicine have been and are presenting the medical profession with new and complex moral dilemmas. To meet the challenge, medical ethics has become a discipline and an acceptable course in the curricula of colleges, universities, medical schools, and seminaries.

Among the pioneers in the development of American medical ethics are W. L. Sperry and Joseph Fletcher. Theirs and other studies in the ethics of medicine was stimulated, in part, by the Nazi medical experiments and crimes. Sperry's work, published in 1950, attempts to answer some moral questions put to him by physicians at the Massachusetts General Hospital in Boston. At that time Sperry was Dean of the Divinity School at Harvard University. His responses are concerned with the specialist, the general practitioner, problems of conscience, codes of medical ethics, democratic and totalitarian medicine, truth-telling, and the issue of euthanasia.[18]

Joseph Fletcher, Visiting Professor of Medical Ethics at the University of Virginia at Charlottesville, published *Morals and Medicine* in 1954. This work deals with five moral dilemmas of the physician: the patient's right to know the truth, the right to birth control, the right to overcome childlessness by artificial insemination, the right to foreclose parenthood by sterilization, and euthanasia or the right to die with

---

[17]Chauncey D. Leake, ed., *Percival's Medical Ethics* (Hunting, NY: Robert E. Krieger Publishing Co., 1927, 1975), p. 101.

[18]W. L. Sperry, *The Ethical Basis of Medical Practice* (New York: Paul B. Hoeber, Inc., 1950).

dignity. These issues have a religious dimension, and Fletcher's work is a Protestant counterbalance to the able Roman Catholic writings on these subjects.[19]

In the last decade there has been something of an explosion of literature in medical ethics. There are a number of journals, books, magazines, and dictionaries on the subject, and an encyclopedia of medical ethics has recently been published. A *summa* of medical ethics entitled *Encyclopedia of Bioethics* was published in 1978. It consists of four large volumes covering topics all the way from abortion to zygote.[20]

Two highly respected institutions for research in medical ethics should be mentioned. The Institute of Society, Ethics and Life Sciences, founded in 1969, is located at Hastings-on-Hudson in New York. It is staffed with competent scholars and publishes the *Hastings Center Report* (formerly *Hastings Center Studies*). In 1971 the Joseph P. Kennedy, Jr. Foundation established the Kennedy Institute of Ethics, Center for Bioethics, at Georgetown University, in Washington, D.C. It, too, is staffed with experts in the field of philosophy and ethics. This institute provides opportunity for both health professionals and those doing advanced studies in the humanities to do graduate study in bioethics.

The discipline of medical ethics is now well established in colleges, universities, institutes, and medical schools. Medical ethics is now an essential part of medical practice. It has evolved from the status of etiquette to a discipline in ethics.

Religion and Medical Ethics

Jewish medical ethics has a long tradition, drawing from two basic sources: the Torah and the Talmud. "Torah" is a general term for divine instruction and guidance. Particularly, the Torah is a standard term for the Pentateuch, the first five books of the Old Testament, containing the Law of Moses. The Talmud is the written story of biblical interpretation and of the making of bylaws and counsel, which covers a period of about one thousand years.

Jewish ethics is firmly rooted in the law and is legally oriented. However, it is not legalistic. The law is an expression of the eternal

---

[19]Joseph Fletcher, *Morals and Medicine* (Boston: Beacon Press, 1954).

[20]Warren T. Reich, editor-in-chief, *Encyclopedia of Bioethics* (New York: The Free Press, 1978).

demand of God to imitate Him and to walk in His ways. God is to be imitated in his attributes of mercy, kindness, justice, humility and love— all of which are qualities revealed in the Torah.[21]

Progressive Jews see the specific laws of the Torah as responses to, rather than the content of, divine revelation. Hence, the demands of morality are absolute, but the specific laws are relative. If specific laws no longer express ethical values which tradition teaches due to changing situations, the laws must be revised.[22] Jewish ethics, therefore, is situational as well as legal in its orientation.

In Jewish ethics the stress is on justice equally applied without regard to persons. Jewish ethics demands equal justice and respect for the dignity of persons. The theological basis for this concept is that all persons are equally made in the image of God. Love also is central in Jewish ethics. "To love one's neighbor as oneself," declared Mordecai Kaplan, "is to call forth in him the fullest use of whatever power God has endowed him with."[23]

Through the centuries these ethical guidelines have found expression in Jewish medical ethics. While no one attitude exists within Judaism with reference to the emerging biomedical problems, there is a growing body of literature by Jewish scholars dealing specifically with such issues as abortion, artificial insemination, euthanasia, eugenics, human medical experimentation, and organ transplantation.[24]

Since the Middle Ages, Roman Catholic theologians and moral philosophers have been wrestling with ethical issues in medicine. As early as the eighteenth century authors wrote about developments in embryology, reproduction, and physician-patient relations. By the nineteenth century a large body of literature had been produced by Catholics relating to medical ethics. The general works fall into the areas of moral theology, medical sciences, and pastoral medicine. The flow of Catholic works on medical ethics has continued to this day.

----

[21]Seymour Siegel, "Ethics and Halakay," *Conservative Judaism* 30 (Spring 1971): 23-24.

[22]Ibid., p. 35.

[23]"A Philosophy of Jewish Ethics," *The Jews II* (New York: Harper and Brothers, 1960), p. 1037.

[24]See Immanuel Jakobovits, *Jewish Medical Ethics* (New York: Philosophical Library, 1959); and Ben Zion Basker, "Problems in Bio-Medical Ethics: A Jewish Perspective," *Judaism* 24 (Spring 1975): 134-43.

According to Fr. Charles Curran, Professor of Moral Theology, Catholic University of America, Catholic interest in medical ethics stems from four factors: (1) Medical ethics has been seen as a "handmaiden of faith" and hence not in opposition to it; (2) Catholic theology stresses the importance of works and is concerned with the minute details of human conduct; (3) Catholic moral theology is in the service of the Sacrament of Penance which deals with the issues arising out of the medical vocation; and (4) because Catholics view the sacrament of baptism as necessary to salvation for all persons including the child in the womb, embryology enters this circle of concern.[25]

Bernard Häring, a Catholic theologian, has written a significant work in medical ethics reflecting the response of contemporary Catholic scholars to the new developments in biomedicine.[26] Häring sees the theologian as a sort of mediator in the interdisciplinary dialogue but with the physician, generally speaking, making the specific decision in each particular situation. Thus he grants a high degree of autonomy to the doctor. Häring sets within the framework of theology the morality of the doctor and such issues as sterilization, abortion, contraception, death, organ transplantation, euthanasia, experimentation on human beings, and homosexuality.

Protestants have not been as interested as Catholics or Jews in medical ethics. This is due to the nature of medicine itself. Until recently the only function of medicine was to help the patient get well. But biomedical technologies have raised moral dilemmas that did not exist in the past. Until the middle of this century, the purpose of medicine, as far as Protestants were concerned, was to cure the sick and to care for the dying. With the new developments in biomedical technologies and the consequent appearance of related moral issues, several volumes on medical ethics have been written by persons who have a Protestant orientation.

Paul Ramsey is a prolific writer in medical ethics. Without any embarrassment he opts for the Christian perspective with a Protestant stance in medical ethics. Ramsey's Lyman Beecher Lectures at Yale Divinity School were published in 1970 as *The Patient as a Person*. In this volume Ramsey discusses a number of moral problems in medicine.

---

[25]"An Overview of Medical Ethics," *New Catholic World* 219:1313 (September/ October 1976).

[26]Bernard Häring, *Medical Ethics* (Notre Dame, IN: Fides Publishing Co., 1973).

Among these are informed consent, research on children, death, the care of the dying, human organ transplantation, and the allocation of spare parts when they are in insufficient supply. The work reflects a Protestant theological and ethical orientation.[27]

James Gustafson, University Professor of Theological Ethics, University of Chicago, attempts to describe the relation of theology to medical ethics. His Pere Marquette Lectures at Marquette University were published in 1975 as *The Contribution of Theology to Medical Ethics*. This is one of the few works dealing specifically with theology and medical ethics. For Gustafson, theology is the reflection upon that human experience (denoted as religious) that senses a relationship to ultimate power. In other words, theology is an intellectual discipline that operates within a religious consciousness, and refers to an ultimate power standing over against as well as sustaining the creation. In this case the ultimate power is the God of biblical revelation. Ethics is also, for Gustafson, reflection upon human experience in its moral dimensions. Medicine specifies the area of human action of which morality is a dimension. Medical ethics relates to this area.

Gustafson maintains that three theological themes pertain to ethics: (1) God intends the well-being of creation; (2) God is both ordering the power that preserves and sustains the well-being of creation and the power that creates new possibilities; and (3) human beings are finite "sinful" agents who determine whether or not the well-being of creation is sustained and fulfilled. How, then, does theology contribute to medical ethics? It provides a moral point of view, a theological answer to the question: "Why be moral?" The answer is, because the ultimate power, God, intends that behavior conform to his purposes and activities for the well-being of creation. Gustafson concedes that the significance of theology's contribution to medical ethics is likely to be greatest for those who share in that religious consciousness, who have an experience of the reality of God.[28] This is true, of course, because the secular humanist would not accept Gustafson's presuppositions about God as ultimate power. Nevertheless Gustafson has clarified to some degree the relationship of theology of the Judeo-Christian tradition to medical ethics.

---

[27]Paul Ramsey, *The Patient as a Person* (New Haven: Yale University Press, 1970).

[28]James Gustafson, *The Contribution of Theology to Medical Ethics* (Milwaukee: Marquette University Press, 1975).

In summary, this overview of medical ethics reveals that the physician has a long tradition of ethics as seen in the numerous codes from Hippocrates to the present. It is clear that medical morality has matured from the status of *etiquette* to that of *ethics*. New technological discoveries will continue, and new ethical issues in medicine will continue to confront the physician. The challenge of new moral dilemmas must be met with relevant ethical guidelines and the vision of hope.

CHAPTER 2

Toward a Model for
Moral Decision Making

Recent advances in biomedical technologies have thrust upon us both ethical concern and confusion. Technology has sped forward like a runner of the Olympics while ethical application to tame that technology and direct it toward making and keeping humanity healthy has limped along on crutches. Hence there is a growing gap between traditional ethics and technological issues. The area of genetics alone bristles with moral problems. For example, no clear ethical perspective exists for our understanding of the issues related to DNA such as "gene splicing." We have been ushered into the "Genetic Age" without an adequate ethical frame of reference and relevant norms of action.

In short we are saddled with ethical ambiguity and uncertainty. Even the nontechnological moral issues that confront the doctor are becoming increasingly complex due to legal restrictions and malpractice lawsuits. Informed consent, for example, is required by law so that the patient will be fully informed about procedure, treatment, and possible side effects. But is it possible for the patient to be "fully informed" about his or her illness? How much informed consent is "reasonable" for the doctor to avoid a lawsuit?

In this chapter some of the current ethical approaches to moral decision making will be briefly examined. Then another model for moral decision making will be presented. Finally, an ethical guideline in making moral decisions in the health care enterprise will be suggested.

Alternative Ethical Systems

The search for an authentic ethic for dealing with the moral issues in medicine and in our common life has resulted in a number of models. I shall briefly comment about some of these and then suggest another approach to moral issues.

First, there is legalism as an approach to making moral decisions. This is a popular method. The legalist insists: "I go by the book." Laws are universalized and applied regardless of the situation. All answers to ethical questions are found in a book of rules. In this approach one does not have to wrestle with the ambiguity of ethics. The law is the law and must be strictly applied from the book. All the doctor has to do is to consult the "medical Robert's Rules of Order" and the decision is made.

At the other end of the ethics spectrum is antinomianism (against the law). The antinomianist is opposed to all laws, rules, and absolute standards of conduct. Existentialism is a form of antinomianism. The existentialist declares: "I choose, therefore I am." He sets up his own moral standards to live by and makes decisions in accordance with these standards. There are no absolute, transcendent ethical norms of conduct. Decisions are made *ad hoc* in each situation.

Paul, the apostle, did battle with the libertines, the Gnostics, and other antinomianists. Jean-Paul Sartre and Albert Camus, French existentialists, represent modern forms of antinomianism. They reject the validity of principles, ethical norms, and the absolutizing of laws. For the antinomian, every situation is unique and discontinuous, and decisions are made extemporaneously.

Emotivism is another form of antinomianism. The emotivist declares: "I go by my feelings." Philosophers of logical positivism, like A. J. Ayer, in his work, *Language, Truth and Logic*, hold that ethical statements only express the speaker's feelings. For example, the statement, "You ought not to steal" really means, "I don't like stealing." Unless statements can be empirically verified, they are meaningless. Ethics, in this case, is based on feelings rather than objective norms. A bumper sticker sums it up nicely: "If it feels good, do it." Or as Hemingway declared in his novel, *Death in the Afternoon*, "What is moral is what you feel good after and what is immoral is what you feel bad after."

On the ethical spectrum between legalism and antinomianism one finds a number of models of moral decision making. There is principlism. The principlist assserts: "I act in accordance with principles." Ethical motifs such as love, justice, and humility may be adopted as guidelines of conduct and action. Love, for example, was the chief ethical principle of John, the apostle, Walter Rauschenbusch, and others. Justice was central in the thought of the Hebrew prophet Amos, and of John Rawls, a social philosopher of Harvard.

Utilitarianism as a model for moral decision making is well-known in the western world. The utilitarianist asserts: "I act in such a way as to make for the greatest good to the greatest number of people." John Stuart Mill and Jeremy Bentham in the last century promoted a form of social hedonism. According to them, moral choices are to be made that will be the most beneficial to the most people. Our democratic government embodies much of the spirit and principle of utilitarianism.

Situationism, or the so-called "new morality" as espoused by Joseph Fletcher and others, has become exceedingly popular with physicians and young people in this country. Fletcher provided a clear expression of this model in his work: *Situation Ethics: The New Morality* (1966). The situationist views love as the only absolute, intrinsic norm of conduct. There are no prefabricated rules or laws that apply in every situation. One must be ready to jettison all rules if love is better served. Adultery, killing, lying, stealing may be the most loving thing to do, depending on the circumstances.

Some are situationists without being aware of it. After listening to my lecture on alternative ethical systems, a medical student said that his approach was not treated. "And what is your ethical posture?" I asked. He replied: "I fly by the seat of my pants." I asked that he provide an example. Then he related that a woman had given birth to a stillborn baby in the General Hospital and he refused to tell her for fear she would go into shock. Yet the rule in the OB-GYN department was to inform all mothers about their newborns. Instead he gave the mother an injection to make her sleep. Obviously he was a situationist and thought that the most loving thing to do in that situation was to follow the procedure he did, even though it violated hospital rules.

Creative Love: Contextual and Principled

Each of the above ethical methodologies has its merits and demerits. No one approach to moral issues is wholly adequate. One must develop one's own way of doing ethics. I opt for principlism, *mutatis mutandis* (the necessary things being changed), as a model in moral decision making. This method I call *contextual principled-agapism*.[1] It lies somewhere between the polarized postures of legalism and antinomianism on the ethical spectrum. It rejects legalism which tends to give law priority over persons; moreover, it can never provide enough rules for the multiplicity of situations in which moral decisions must be made. At the other end of the spectrum, this approach rejects all forms of antinomianism as being too egocentric.

Aspects of Contextual Principled-Agapism. Some explanation of contextual principled-agapism is in order. The "contextual" dimension of this ethical methodology relates to the whole situation, background, or environment relevant to a happening. Moral decisions are made in real, concrete situations and they are determined to some degree by the context. It is, therefore, in a sense, a gestalt decision.

Moral decisions are made in the context of faith as well as the facts. For the religious person the context of faith is theological. It is "faith (in God) acting in love" (Galatians 5:6). The secular humanist also acts in faith, faith in himself, or in the laws of nature, of mind, of reason, or of nontranscendent reality. In short, everyone—regardless of religious or nonreligious orientation—acts on the basis of faith.

The term "principled" involves a clear distinction between principle and rule. A rule specifies what is to be done in a particular situation. A principle is more general: like a compass, it gives direction but not a detailed roadmap.

"Agapism" is derived from the Greek term *agape* (love). Agape is the central ethical motif of the Judeo-Christian faith. Agape-love is nowhere specifically defined in the Old or New Testaments. But considered in its total context of Scripture, love appears to mean—in relation to God—reverence, trust, and obedience on the part of His people. In relation to

---

[1]Cf. Harmon L. Smith and Lewis W. Hodges, *The Christian and His Decisions* (Nashville: Abingdon Press, 1969), "Introduction," pp. 11-33, for the concept of principled contextualism. For the concept of "obedient" and in-principled agapism see Paul Ramsey, *Basic Christian Ethics* (New York: Charles Scribners, 1950).

God's creatures and creation, love means *to will their well-being.* One's well-being includes, among other things, human dignity, health, basic rights, justice, and freedom within responsibility. With reference to creation, it means *care for the good earth and the things that grow upon it.* "Principled-agapism" is love expressing itself in the form of such basic principles which provide it with direction, structure, and concreteness.

Agape-love wills not only the well-being of others and the environment, but also of *self.* The "Great Commandment" includes love of God, neighbor, and self (Luke 10:27). Self-love, therefore, is not selfishness or selfism. Eric Fromm has made it clear that the lover is a human self, too, and does not exclude love of self. Love of self is inseparably related to love for any other being.[2] He goes on to note that self-love and selfishness are opposites and that selfish persons are incapable of loving either themselves or others. Respect for others is a component of love. One can respect others only to the degree of one's own self-respect.[3]

Love is an ethical imperative in Judaism and has its roots in the Old Testament. It includes love of enemies as well as fellow Israelites (Leviticus 19:18; Exodus 23:4ff.). Love of God and neighbor are inseparable (Deuteronomy 6:4; Leviticus 19:18). Love is an energy which flows along the lines of a triangle whose points are God, self, and neighbor.[4] Loving God means keeping His commandments, serving Him, and walking in His ways (Deuteronomy 10:12; 19:9; 30:16). True worship consists of the practice of justice, love of mercy, and a humble walk with God (Micah 6:8).

In the Judeo-Christian faith the ground of love is the God of revelation. God's ontological nature is that of love (1 John 4:8) and the God of love demands love of the neighbor (1 John 4:11). The very nature of God is to will the well-being of his children who in turn will the well-being of others.

Jesus taught in terms of principles; agape was the leitmotiv of his life and ministry. He laid down basic principles, not rules, for the implementation of love. The principles of the value of personhood, brotherhood, and servanthood as the idea of greatness are basic principles through which agape expresses itself. He summed up all the law and the prophets

---

[2]Eric Fromm, *The Art of Loving* (New York: Bantam Books, 1963), pp. 48-53.

[3]Harry S. Sullivan, "Selfishness and Self-love," *Psychiatry* 2 (1939): 507, 523.

[4]J. R. Coates, ed., *Bible Key Words* (New York: Harper and Brothers, 1951), p. 42.

in terms of love to God, neighbor and self, a concept he inherited from Jewish tradition. He concluded that all rules, laws, and principles "hang" upon love (Matthew 22:40). Love is central; all other moral teachings are commentary.

In the New Testament, Jesus nowhere defines love. He illustrated, exemplified, and incarnated love. It is clear that God's will is love (agape). Love is inclusive of neighbors and enemies (Matthew 5:43-48). Love requires involvement in the needs of others, as illustrated in the story of the Good Samaritan (Luke 10:29-37). Love is existential, relating oneself to God in the interest of others. Love can be commanded by Jesus Christ because it is an act of the will. In contrast to agape-love, sentimental, emotional, or fleeting love cannot be commanded.

Love's characteristics are manifested in Paul's ode to agape (1 Corinthians 13). Among other things, love's content consists of justice, truth, trust, care, regard, forgiveness, and fair play. It is patient and kind; and not jealous, boastful, arrogant, rude, irritable, or resentful; and it rejoices in the right. These are instruments of the love that wills the well-being of self and of others.

In contextual principled-agapism, love utilizes principles, laws, and rules as instruments in a particular situation. Justice, for example, gives structure and direction to love. So do truth, goodness, kindness, and other principles as indicated above. When rules conflict, love takes priority. Love may take priority over truth when a human life is at stake. Those in Europe who harbored Jews in their homes during the Nazi era were morally justified when they lied to the Nazi stormtroopers, telling them that no Jews were there. In the first place, Nazis who murdered millions of people were not worthy of the truth. Secondly, when the choice is between saving a human life or telling the truth, as a general principle, the most loving thing to do is to save a life.

The Holy Spirit in both Old and New Testaments is the Spirit of justice and liberty. Compare the announcement of Jesus, a direct quotation from Isaiah 61:1-2:

> The Spirit of the Lord is upon me,
> because he has anointed me to preach
>   good news to the poor.
> He has sent me to proclaim release to
>   the captives

and recovering of sight to the blind,
to set at liberty those who are oppressed,
to proclaim the acceptable year of the Lord
(Luke 4:18-19, RSV).

In both Old and New Covenants the Spirit is the power of God energizing our lives and encouraging us to act justly, to love mercy, and to liberate those in bondage. The Spirit is not merely something for our ecstatic enjoyment, but a power for ethical action. The Spirit provides strength and skills to individuals and leads to the truth.[5]

Methodology. As to a methodology for the implementation of love, a bifocal approach is essential. This method looks to the sciences for facts, that is, for *what is,* and to the norms of the Scriptures for *what ought to be.* When all the facts possible about an issue are known, love, in terms of willing the well-being of others, becomes the principle of judgment and action. With knowledge of the context, one decides which principles love can employ to make for the well-being of the other. Obviously, reason is essential in making moral decisions. Love and knowledge go together in making decisions and attempting to deal with the issues of life. Knowledge about an issue and its context is essential for intelligent action.

Such an approach to moral problems has some distinct advantages. Where the Bible and other sacred literature do not speak directly to issues raised by biomedical technologies such as the transplant of organs in humans, recombinant DNA (gene splicing to create new organisms), and genetic manipulation, one must seek for ethical guidelines in harmony with agape. Again, this method in ethics saves one from legalism on the one hand and antinomianism or no law on the other. It delivers one from subjectivism by providing basic guiding principles of action. Law without love leads to a dead legalism; love without law leads to subjectivism. Finally, even without the theological dimension in decision making, the secular humanist should be able to accept love as willing the well-being of others.

Love as a Therapeutic Force. The creative and therapeutic powers of love have been known for centuries. Numerous scholars today have

---

[5]Karl Barth, *The Faith of the Church* (New York: Meridian Books, 1958), p. 128.

documented love's healing role in human life. A minimum of love is essential to the survival of babies and their normal growth. The Harvard Research Center in Creative Altruism Studies has shown that love tends to increase longevity.[6] Deficiency of "the vitamin of love" is responsible for many mental disorders.[7] Psychiatrists are becoming increasingly aware of the curative power of love. The research of G. W. Allport, K. E. Appel, F. E. Fiedler, Carl Rogers, Viktor Frankl, H. J. Eysenck, and others show that the establishment of a relationship of empathy, sympathy, kindness, and mutual trust between therapist and patient make up the core of the curative agent in the treatment of mental disorders.[8]

I personally have witnessed the curative force of creative love. Patients have come to the psychiatric ward where I work feeling that no one, in the words of the psalmist, "cared for my soul." An expression of love, care, concern, and respect for patients has proven to be a basic component in the healing process. A nine-year-old child was admitted to the hospital. I saw her after she had been a patient for several days. As I passed by her wheel chair, I greeted her and patted her on the shoulder. She smiled and returned my greeting. A chaplain standing nearby remarked: "When she was first admitted she would have bitten your hand." I learned that she was an unwanted and abused child who was angry and bitter when admitted to the hospital. What brought about the radical change in her life? She had been assigned to an elderly woman, a surrogate mother, who expressed tender love for her. Loving care had helped to transform an angry child into a happy, outgoing human being.

The Golden Principle: Moral Guideline in Medicine

"Do unto others as you would have them do unto you," the "Golden Rule," is another form of the imperative to love God, neighbor, and self. It is really not a rule but a principle, for it does not spell out specific actions in the treatment of others. Hence, it might be called the "Golden Principle." As such it is a universal ethical guideline. This guideline appears in one form or another in the major religions, philosophies, and psychologies of the world. Thus it provides love with a universal principle

---

[6]Pitirm Sorokin, "The Powers of Creative Unselfish Love," in Abraham Maslow, ed., *New Knowledge in Human Values* (New York: Harper and Brothers, 1959), p. 6.

[7]Ibid., p. 7.

[8]Ibid., p. 8.

for both religious and nonreligious persons. Agape-love in the Christian sense does not produce, as theologian John Macquarrie observes, "a kind of love that is fundamentally different from the love that may be found among non-Christians."[9] Yet there is a difference. For those in the Judeo-Christian faith, love is grounded in God and has an eternal and cosmic meaning. For the nonbeliever love is anthropocentric and has a "this worldly" significance alone.

Obviously there are some thinkers who reject the Golden Principle as an outmoded and irrelevant moral guideline. George Bernard Shaw, for example, levels the following criticism at the principle: "Do not do to others as you would that they should do unto you. Their tastes may not be the same."[10] Some misinterpret it. A popular rendition has it: "Do the other fellow before he does you." Yet this principle provides a common moral norm for peoples around the world as expressed in their writings and behavior.

Religious Expressions of the Golden Principle. Jewish religious literature gives a negative formulation to the Golden Principle. It appears, for example, in Tobit 4:15: "What you hate, do not to anyone." A Gentile asked Rabbi Hillel to teach him the whole law while standing on one foot. The Rabbi replied: "What you would not have done to yourself, do not to another. That is the whole law, the rest is commentary" (Shabbath 31a). In the Palestinian Targum, the Golden Principle is used to explain loving one's neighbor.[11] The love of one's neighbor indicates that positive aspects of the principle were also taught.

In the Christian tradition, the Golden Principle appears in both positive and negative forms. Jesus' version is positive: "So whatever you wish that men would do to you, do so to them" (Matthew 7:12, RSV; also Luke 6:31). According to Matthew 7:12, the principle is a summary of the "law and the prophets." It is universal in scope and must be correlated with the other teachings of Jesus.

Paul, the apostle of Jesus, puts the rule in negative form: "Love does no wrong to a neighbor" (Romans 13:10, RSV). In some of the earliest

---

[9]John Macquarrie, *Three Issues in Ethics* (New York: Harper and Row, 1970), p. 133.

[10]*Collected Plays With Their Prefaces* (New York: Dodd, Mead, and Co., 1975), 2:781.

[11]Cited by Eusebius in *Preparation for the Gospel*, 8.7.6.

church documents, it is stated both negatively and positively by the writers.[12]

The principle appears in numerous other religions. In Buddhism, it reads: "Hurt not others in ways that you yourself would find hurtful" (Udana-Varga). Brahmanism has it: "Do nought unto others which would cause you pain if done to you" (Mahabharata). Confucianism puts it: "What I do not wish to have done unto me, I likewise wish not to do to others."[13]

Taoism relates the principle specifically to one's neighbor: "Regard your neighbor's gain as your own gain, and your neighbor's loss as your own loss" (T'ai Shang Kan Ying P'ien). Zoroastrianism formulates it: "That nature alone is good which refrains from doing unto another whatsoever is not good for itself" (Dadistan-I-Dinik). And in Islam, it is: "No one of you is a believer until he desires for his brother that which he desires for himself" (Sunna).

Philosophical and Psychological Expressions of the Golden Principle. Agape in terms of the Golden Principle appears in the thought and writings of the great philosophers, social scientists, and psychiatrists. Immanuel Kant, German philosopher, placed it at the heart of the categorical imperative. "So act," Kant wrote, "as to treat humanity, whether in thine own person or in that of any other, in every case as an end withal, never as a means only."[14] Robert MacIver, Lieber Professor Emeritus of Political Philosophy and Sociology of Columbia University, declares that the Golden Principle is the only universal ethic "that stands by itself in the light of its own reason, the only rule that can stand by itself in the naked, warring universe, in the face of contending values of men and groups."[15] MacIver says that the universal within the rule is one of procedure which prescribes not a goal of action but a mode of behaving. On the level of goals and values, he thinks that there is an irreconcilable

---

[12]Irenaeus, "Against Heresies," book 3, ch. 12, p. 14; and Tertullian, "Against Marcion," book 4, ch. 16.

[13]Analects, V:11 in Charles Eliot, ed., *Sacred Writings*, vol. 44 in *The Harvard Classics* (New York: Collier, 1910), p. 16.

[14]Immanuel Kant, *Fundamental Principles of the Metaphysic of Morals* (New York: The Liberal Arts Press, 1949), p. 46.

[15]"The Deep Beauty of the Golden Rule," in Ruth Anshen, ed., *Moral Principles of Action* (New York: Harper and Brothers, 1952), pp. 41-42.

conflict. The rule does not attack the will and goals of the other person, but provides a new dimension for them. MacIver thus formulates the Rule: "Do as *you* would will others to do." See yourself, he says, in the place of others, and others in your place. "Reciprocity of restraint" (a key phrase of MacIver's) from evil does both individuals good.[16]

Psychiatrist Erik H. Erikson of Harvard presented a series of lectures at the University of Delhi and the International Centre in 1963. His final address was entitled "The Golden Rule in the Light of New Insight." Erikson holds that the Rule advocates that one should do (or not do) to another what one wishes to be (or not to be) done by. Thus, to identify self-interest and the interest of other selves, the Rule alternately employs the method of warning, "Do *not* as you would *not* be done by," and of exhortation, "Do, as you would be done by." Erikson proceeds to apply the Rule to various stages in individual maturation. He interprets the Rule to say "that it is best to do to another what will strengthen you even as it will strengthen" the other person and will develop his best potentials even as it develops one's own. He then applies this concept of the Rule to the healer and patient relationships, to economics, and to the international situation.[17]

Another psychiatrist, Freida Fromm-Reichmann, defines her concept of "mature love," as do Erich Fromm and Harry Stack Sullivan, in terms of the Golden Rule. Her psychological formulation of the Rule asserts that it is "the state of interpersonal relatedness in which one is as concerned with the growth, maturation, welfare, and happiness of the beloved person as one is with one's own."[18] But some would question whether her formula expresses "mature love," for it appears to be limited to "the beloved person" to the exclusion of others.

Maurice Levine, another distinguished psychiatrist who has written much in the areas of ethics and psychiatry notes that the Golden Rule has some strengths as well as some basic weaknesses. His chief criticism is that it makes one's own feelings the criterion of moral decision making. It makes, in short, one's self the judge. So Levine concludes that the Rule must be "cross-checked" at times by other forms of "creative ethics," that

---

[16]Ibid.

[17]Erik H. Erikson, *Insight and Responsibility* (New York: W. W. Norton and Co., 1964), ch. 6.

[18]Freida Fromm-Reichmann, *Principles of Intensive Psychotherapy* (Chicago: University of Chicago Press, 1950), p. 34.

is, mutual help and interests in consonance with the other for continuing development.[19]

Levine is right. The Golden Rule must be seen in the context of other moral principles. When my son, John, was in elementary school, he came home one day and announced that he had practiced the Golden Rule. Gratified as any proud father would be, I asked him to tell me about it. The class had been given a test and his best friend sitting behind John did not know a particular answer. So John gave it to him. My son reasoned that if *he* had not known the answer, he would have wanted his friend to share it with *him*. For John that was the meaning of: "Do unto others as you would wish them to do unto you." I explained to him that the Rule must be correlated with and seen in the context of the other ethical teachings such as honesty and justice—a heavy concept for a fifth-grader!

Summary. Love in terms of the Golden Principle appears in the major religions and philosophies of the world. It is derived from agape-love from which all other ethical imperatives are derived in the Judeo-Christian tradition. Hence, this approach to ethics is neither pure act-agapism (no rules) nor rule-agapism. Rather it is contextual principled-agapism in which justice, fair play, reciprocity, mutual trust, and so forth become instruments of love. Both religious and non-religious physicians will find love in this sense to be a valid ethical guideline in the practice of medicine. It is in keeping with much of the ethical teachings of the Hippocratic Oath. A primary promise in the Oath is that the physician will "do no harm" to the patient. The apostle Paul expresses it this way: "Love hurts nobody" (Romans 13:10, Phillips).

---

[19]Maurice Levine, *Psychiatry and Ethics* (New York: George Braziller, 1972), p. 107ff.

CHAPTER 3

Ethics in Physician-Patient Relations

"Physician, heal thy image." In substance this was the theme of Norman Cousins, former editor of *Saturday Review* and author of the popular book, *Anatomy of an Illness*, in a recent address to the University of Louisville Medical School seniors. Cousins had survived a usually fatal disease after rebelling against traditional hospital therapy. He urged the would-be doctors to approach patients as individuals and maintained that failure to do so is a basic cause for the current criticism heaped upon health care professionals. He suggested that treating patients as persons would not only contribute significantly to their health, but also would do more than any public relations campaign for the new doctor's image with the public they serve.[1]

In this chapter I shall stress physician-patient relations as a covenantal partnership. Both physician and patient are persons; their interpersonal relations should be consonant with the concept of personhood. In developing this theme we need to deal with the image and role of the

---

[1]*The Louisville Times*, 28 May 1980, p. A7.

physician, the patient as a person, and the physician and patient as partners in the healing process.

The Patient as a Person

"Person" is a much abused term. It is a word that is bandied about by psychologists, psychiatrists, philosophers, and theologians without telling us what it means.

Etymologically the term is derived from the Latin *persona*, a mask worn by actors in ancient times. In the spacious Greek theaters it was difficult for audiences to discern expressions in dramatic performances. Hence, masks were used, often with megaphone mouthpieces. The mask was worn by the ancient actor to identify the mood of the character being protrayed. The mask was called a *persona*, a term which eventually came to mean the actor himself.

C. C. Jung, the psychiatrist, adopted the term *persona* to express personage, which, for him, denotes the *cloak* of personality assumed by an individual in contrast to the *real* personality he called "soul." Swiss psychiatrist Paul Tournier uses Jung's conception of personage to designate the social facade assumed by an individual to prevent others from observing the real self.[2] According to Tournier, person and personage are linked together, but distinct, and the person can be approached only by stripping away the personage. For Tournier, the real person can be revealed only through living dialogue between man and man and between man and God.[3]

Nicolai Hartmann becomes specific when he defines a person as "a subject that can discern values, cultivate attitudes toward them, and pursue them by voluntary action."[4] A recovery of this ethical dimension of the person is imperative in the light of increasing doubt about the significance and sacredness of the individual human being. Forces depersonalizing personhood must be humanized and made to enhance persons.

In order to recover the meaning of *person*, in the midst of our dehumanizing structures, the concept must include transmoral and trans-

---

[2]*The Meaning of Persons* (New York: Harper and Brothers, 1957), pp. 5-22.

[3]Ibid., p. 15.

[4]Virgilius Ferm, ed., *Encyclopedia of Morals* (New York: Philosophical Library, 1956), p. 205.

cendent dimensions. Therefore, a person must be seen as a whole individual made in the *imago Dei* with inherent worth, moral responsibility, and the right to self-fulfillment. The inherent worth of an individual must be revered not only because of the transcendent element, but because of his or her humanity regardless of race, class, religion, and ideology.

Man is a psychosomatic whole, a *Thou*, not merely an *it*. Martin Buber, the philosophical theologian, has noted that we tend to relate at two levels; the levels of I-Thou and I-It. To relate at the It level is to make a person a thing, an object to be manipulated. A husband can treat his wife (and vice versa) as an "it." A physician can treat his or her patient as a thing. An employer may treat employees as "hands." I was called a "hand" when I went to work in a southern cotton mill at the age of thirteen, weighing seventy-four pounds. I worked ten hours each day for five and one-half days per week with one week off for vacation. Management gave little thought in those days to the welfare of "hands," or to the fact that these "hands" actually were persons with heads, hearts, and spirits. Rather, the machine was more important than the man. The man was as much a means to an end as any of the inanimate machinery, and equally expendable. He could be injured or "fired" without any compensation.

This depersonalization syndrome can find expression in the health care field. But the physician is to treat the whole individual, not just diabetes, or pneumonia, or an infected foot. As Paul Tournier has declared, the doctor's task is only half done if he does not "help the patient to help solve the problems in his life."[5] Otherwise the patient is treated for the disease and not its possibly non-physical cause or causes— emotional and psychological, such as grief, guilt, or numerous other causes.

The physician and members of his staff are also persons made in the *imago Dei*. They are to be treated in accordance with the principles of respect, trust, and care as long as they prove to be competent and concerned about the well-being of their patients. Physician-patient relations should be characterized by an ethic of reciprocity of the Golden Rule. Patients need to trust physicians as whole persons and do to them as they would be done by.

---

[5]*The Healing of Persons* (New York: Harper and Row, 1965), p. xiii.

The Physician: Models and Roles

Throughout the history of medicine various models of the physician have appeared. Antiquity produced the "priest-physician." Its contemporary counterpart is echoed in the concept of the physician-patient relationship as being religious. The doctor's office takes on the aura of a sanctuary and the patient views the physician as something of a high priest. In this model, the doctor's authority so dominates the patient that the patient is deprived of his freedom.[6]

The Hippocratic Oaths of ancient Greece (sixth to first centuries B.C.) reflect a "convenantal" model of the physician, faithful to the oath and the covenant in terms of confidentiality, equality in treatment, and avoidance of doing the patient any harm. Its modern counterpart is the contractual or covenant model characterized by true sharing of moral authority, responsibility, and decision making. Basic norms of freedom, dignity, truth telling, promise keeping, and justice are components of the contractual relationship. When significant choices are to be made the patient has freedom to make such decisions.[7]

In the seventeenth and eighteenth centuries, England produced the "Gentleman Doctor." This conceptualization of the physician signified a cluster of ideals about the doctor qua person: for example, the physician should "unite tenderness with steadiness . . . [and] governed sound reason . . . in making a clinical decision about using a new drug or method of surgical treatment."[8] In early America the model developed was that of the "Country Doctor." As the country became more urbanized, the physician tended to become the "Specialist Doctor" with Aesculapian authority.

There is one image of the doctor which has appeared in every generation. It is pointedly expressed in the Latin quatrain ascribed to Duricius Cordus (1486-1544), father of Valerius who discovered ether:

Three faces has the physician:
A god's when first sought;
An angel's, the cure half wrought;

---

[6]Robert M. Veatch, "Models for Ethical Medicine in a Revolutionary Age," *Hastings Center Report* 2:3 (1972): 5-6.

[7]Ibid., p. 7.

[8]Chauncey D. Leake, ed., *Percival's Medical Ethics* (Hunting, NY: Robert E. Krieger Publishing Co., 1975), pp. 15, i, xii.

But when comes due the doctor's fee,
Then Satan looks less terrible than he![9]

The roles of the physician in relation to the patient are of a multiple nature. I am indebted to Nancy Flowers, M.D., Chief of Cardiology, University of Louisville School of Medicine, for the following suggested functions of the physician:

• He or she is a coach. As such the physician manifests an attitude of confidence that the patient will win.

• The patient needs a sense of security and the doctor becomes a father figure of assurance that all is going to be well, that the individual has a good chance of coming through surgery. The doctor fulfills the role of a father to help the patient to enter with a measure of calmness and confidence the intervention of surgery.

The Doctor's Roles

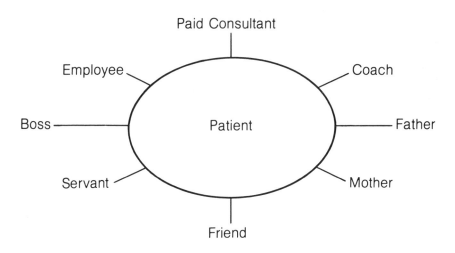

[9]Ibid., p. xlii.

●As a mother figure, the physician serves in terms of an understanding, empathetic, and caring person.

• The physician also functions as a friend, as an adult to an adult. Peership provides the patient with the awareness that someone relates and understands.

• The doctor serves also in the role of a consultant paid by the patient who deserves to get the facts about his or her situation, for example, the chances of survival during cardiac catheterization, open heart surgery, or a coronary bypass; the problems of convalescence related to surgery; and whether or not the operation usually results in the extension, and a better quality, of life.

• In a sense the physician is an employee of the patient. Hence, the patient expects faithful, consistent, and competent care and treatment in the healing process. Being a concerned and warm person toward patients does not compensate for incompetency. While the patient desires these attitudes in his doctor he also wants a doctor with technical skills.

• Finally, there is a sense in which the physician is a boss, an authoritarian figure. Someone must be in charge of the whole process of medical care to give it direction.

Patient-Physician in Covenantal Partnership

A sense of wholeness is the goal of both physician and patient. Health has the inherent meaning of salvation. Indeed, Wycliffe, the famous translator of the Scriptures, translates the Greek word for salvation as health. Health and salvation are closely linked in the Bible. John, the beloved disciple, writing to the early Christians wished "above all things that thou mayest prosper and be in health, even as thy soul prospereth" (3 John 2, KJV).

A resident psychiatrist requested a theological consultation on a patient in the psychiatric clinic. I interviewed the man who looked like a member of Hell's Angels. I identified myself as the theological consultant of the hospital. This patient had no idea what a theological consultant is, but nevertheless proceeded to tell me his story in his words—most of them unprintable. When he finally came to a conversation pit stop, I asked, "What is your religious orientation?" He asked, "What the hell does that have to do with it?" I tried to explain that a person is body, mind, and spirit, and that unless he got these dimensions of his being together, he would not likely get well. He responded, "Damn! I see what you mean."

Physician and patient must work together with the goal of wholeness. Norman Cousins has presented the idea of a partnership model for physician-patient relationships. During his critical illness, Cousins and his doctor became colleagues in seeking to eliminate illness and to preserve health based upon confidence and trust. In this model the patient shares in the choice of therapies. Cousins was fortunate in that his doctor had been a friend of twenty years and "put himself in the place of" his patient. At the same time, Cousins "got into the act" of taking responsibility for his own recovery. He began to utilize faith, hope, love, and laughter—positive emotions—which allegedly produced therapeutic chemical changes in the body.[10]

Cousins's partnership model has some valuable features; but as a whole it is too idealistic to be practical for the general population of patients. Few doctors would or could take time to implement this model in terms of empathy and cooperation with the patient in the choice of therapies. Few patients would have Cousins's knowledge of therapies and how to choose them. And it is doubtful whether many patients want to take on such responsibilities or whether they would have the material resources to facilitate the style of recuperation Mr. Cousins was able to afford.

A synthesis of Cousins's partnership model, Paul Ramsey's covenant model, and Robert Veatch's contract model has some promise. Ramsey holds that the practice of medicine is only one of the many covenants of life. It is a covenant of fidelity with the moral quality and action characterized by justice, fairness, faithfulness, the sanctity of life, love, and like moral principles.[11]

Veatch calls for a contract or covenant model, but interprets covenant more in terms of a contract. He sees it as a relationship in which obligations and benefits are limited in scope. Freedom, dignity, truth telling, promise keeping and justice are essential in the contractual relationship. The patient participates in the decision making process, but not in every trivial decision. If trust and confidence are lost in the relationship, the covenant is broken.

Perhaps a convenantal model can be developed from basic elements of several models. It would consist of a mutually established covenant by

[10]*Anatomy of an Illness: As Perceived by the Patient* (New York: W. W. Norton and Co., 1979), pp. 30-43.

[11]*The Patient as a Person* (New Haven: Yale University Press, 1980).

physician and patient. It would encompass medical care in terms of the doctor's skills and counsels and the patient's will to get well and to stay well. Love, in the sense of willing the well-being of the other, would be the fundamental principle of relationship and action. This would be a covenant of contingency. Failure to keep the covenant on the part of either physician or patient would be grounds for dissolving it.

From love (to will the well-being of the other), a principled force, may be derived several principles of interpersonal relations in the covenantal model. One is that of honesty. The patient honestly describes his condition in terms of symptoms, effects of therapies, and faithfulness or unfaithfulness in following the doctor's advice. On the other hand the physician is to be honest in terms of informed consent, truth telling, and confidentiality.

Acceptance of responsibility for one's own health is another component of the covenantal model. This includes acceptance of a measure of responsibility for one's own recovery from disease or disability. It involves the responsibility of practicing a healthy lifestyle. According to a 1976 report from the U. S. Surgeon General, as many as fifty percent of the deaths in this country that year were due to unhealthy lifestyles. The traditional American way of life—too much eating, too much sugar, too little exercise, too much hard work, too much drinking, and too much smoking, and so forth—has been shown to be deadly.[12]

Another principle that will enhance the ethical quality and facilitate the healing is that of the "therapeutic touch." Occasionally by touching, the health care professional tends to convey a feeling of caring, like stroking a fevered brow or a pat on the arm. Once I was on a collective farm in Russia. When I was shown the dairy, I noticed that a large number of the cows were being milked the old-fashioned way by a number of milkmaids instead of by modern mechanized equipment. When I inquired why machines were not utilized, the man in charge of the dairy replied, "These cows prefer the personal touch." Likewise, patients desire the personal touch of care, understanding, and compassion. The ability to express personal concern for patients is a powerful resource for their healing. Often the warmth of a caring touch can convey this concern. At one particular Louisville hospital, volunteer workers are prohibited from touching the patients. Significantly, however, an excep-

---

[12]Norton-Children's Hospitals *Newsletter* 4:10 (October 1980): 1.

tion is made for volunteers on the oncology unit where most of the patients are faced with the anxiety and pain of cancer. It has been observed that stroking a patient or holding his hand can often have a very therapeutic effect. This contact conveys the important message that someone cares.

A covenantal model calls for the caring *for* as well as the care *of* the patient. Caring does not mean that one has to become sentimental and effusive. Caring is the recognition, regard, and respect for the patient as well as the use of the doctor's skills in the healing process. Much healing is due to personality independent of medical science.

In the covenantal model the patient does everything in his power to enhance the healing of himself. He takes seriously the injunction: "Patient, heal thyself." He must have faith in the effectiveness of the treatment. As a lad in a poverty-level home, I recall that our pharmacopoeia consisted of corn liquor, herbs from the field, and patent medicine for female sickness. When spring rolled around most children got a powerful dose of sulphur and molasses. That knocked all of the winter apathy out of you. When the great "flu" epidemic hit us, we wore asafetida (a gum resin used as a repellent against dogs, cats, and rabbits today) in a cloth bag around our necks to avoid catching the flu. There were seven in my family and we all caught the flu; but we all survived while many in the hills died.

Faith in folk medicine, no doubt, helped our family to survive. Corn liquor for colds was a ready source of medication in our home medicine cabinet. (Some had colds the year round!) A poultice of several pungent items was for sores and boils. When our sides hurt, we turned over a rock, spit on it, put it back and returned to work. A midwife delivered the babies who were, with few exceptions, breast-fed. And the miracle is that most of them survived. I have the opinion that our survival was due to the solidarity of the family as well as parents who not only took care of us but also cared for us.

"Physician, heal thy image" by treating patients as persons. This one act does more to enhance the physician-patient relationship and to help the healing process than anything else. It evokes the trust, confidence, and cooperation of the patient and hastens his healing. Competence should be accompanied by compasssion, medical technology by the human touch. As Francis Peabody, late professor of medicine at Harvard, has so graphically put it: "One of the essential qualities of the clinician is interest in humanity, for the secret of the care of the patient is in caring for the patient."[13]

[13]"The Care of the Patient," *Doctor and Patient* (New York: Macmillan Co., 1930), p. 57.

CHAPTER 4

Loneliness:
An Ethical Issue in Medical Practice

In spite of the prevalence of loneliness as one of the most common afflictions in American life, there is a paucity of serious research concerning this condition. In the late 1950s, as Freida Fromm-Reichman notes, loneliness was "not even mentioned in most psychiatric textbooks."[1] Even the widely used *Comprehensive Textbook of Psychiatry* contains only one reference to loneliness.[2] With few exceptions loneliness has been ignored by the writers of psychological and sociological literature. Loneliness appears usually to be a concomitant factor with other symptoms. But this observation does not remove the obligation (often unrecognized) to diagnose loneliness and its effects case by case. The medical consultant has an ethical responsibility to calculate loneliness into the plan for management in the physician-patient relationship.

---

[1]Frieda Fromm-Reichmann, "Loneliness," *Psychiatry* 22:1 (January 1959):1.

[2]Alfred M. Freedman, et al., *Comprehensive Textbook of Psychiatry-II*, 2nd ed. (Baltimore: Williams & Wilkins Co., 1975).

Why is there more about loneliness in popular songs and commercials than in scientific literature? For one thing, psychiatrists have failed to develop a theoretical basis for coping with numerous manifestations of loneliness. No diagnostic category for loneliness appears in the third edition of *The Diagnostic and Statistical Manual of Mental Disorders* (1980). No adequate taxonomy of types exists. Also this affliction is difficult to conceptualize and to understand. Moreover, society's attitude toward loneliness is that loneliness is primarily a symptom of a weak character, a self-indulgence which should be shrugged off. Hence the popular notion prevails that loneliness is of little medical significance.

Research on loneliness in the last decade, however, reflects a serious effort to get at its nature, source, and management. In 1974, Robert Weiss (Department of Psychiatry, Harvard Medical School) alerted us to the seriousness of the problem by showing the denigrating effects of the experience of emotional and social isolation in his book, *Loneliness: The Experience of Emotional and Social Isolation.*[3] And in 1977, James J. Lynch (a psychologist and director of the Physiological Clinic and Laboratories of the University of Maryland School of Medicine) documented the physical consequences of loneliness in his book, *The Broken Heart: Medical Consequences of Loneliness.*[4]

As a result of the studies by Weiss and Lynch, we now have a more precise conceptual and clinical understanding of loneliness. Its dynamics, physical and emotional consequences, nuances, and effective therapies are becoming more intelligible. Attempting to do a study on this subject, however, is still like making "brick without straw." Hence my contribution will be fragmentary and imprecise: it simply brings together recent findings on the meaning, medical consequences, and management of loneliness.

The Meaning of Loneliness

What do we mean by the term loneliness? How is it to be distinguished from other feelings? Edgar N. Jackson declares that loneliness is "a desperate feeling of separation from those who give meaning to life."[5]

---

[3]*Loneliness: The Experience of Emotional and Social Isolation* (Cambridge: MIT Press, 1974).

[4]*The Broken Heart: Medical Consequences of Loneliness* (New York: Basic Books, 1977).

[5]*The Many Faces of Grief* (Nashville: Abingdon, 1977), p. 30.

But this definition is too narrow because it limits the experience of loneliness to separation from persons. Robert Weiss defines loneliness as the absence of a sense of attachment to someone or something, or the absence of a sense of community. Loneliness is a response to a deficit situation, a deficit of specific relational provisions, emotional and social isolation.[6] For a working definition I define loneliness as *the anguish of being deprived of those relationships which provide meaning to human existence.* Loneliness can take the form of isolation from relationships to a person, a group, a home, a country, an activity, or to God.

In order to more clearly identify loneliness, it must be distinguished from other related feelings. "Grief," for example, is distinguished from loneliness in that grief normally subsides with time; but loneliness persists so long as no new relationship is found to replace the lost one. "Alone" is a neutral term; one can be alone without being lonely. For example, there is the creative aloneness of the artist. On the other hand, one may be alone and desperately lonely. With Coleridge's Ancient Mariner, one may be "alone, alone, all, all alone, on a wide, wide sea" and long for companionship. "Aloneness," in this sense, is a negative term, and the equivalent of loneliness.

Solitude is a state of self-chosen separation from others where we can let down our guard for self-discovery, self-renewal, and new perspectives on our problems. Solitude may be attained by withdrawing into some isolated place, away from our peers and family, for a limited period. But, as Henri J. M. Nouwen notes, "the solitude that really counts is the solitude of the heart; it is an inner quality or attitude that does not depend on physical isolation."[7]

Loneliness may be a component of the depression, grief, guilt, sadness, and/or anger syndromes. Research on loneliness is too piecemeal to adequately understand it as a completely distinct phenomenon. For example, psychiatrists hold divergent views about the motivational consequences of loneliness. Harry S. Sullivan thinks of loneliness as a driving force.[8] Frieda Fromm-Reichmann and others argue that lonely people

---

[6]Weiss, *Loneliness*, pp. 227-28.

[7]*Reaching Out* (New York: Doubleday and Co., 1975), p. 25.

[8]*The Interpersonal Theory of Psychiatry* (New York: Norton, 1953). Also, William A. Sadler, Jr., "The Causes of Loneliness," *Psychology and Personal Growth*, ed. Abe Arkoff (Boston: Allyn and Bacon, 1980), p. 130.

are apathetic, passive, and depressed.[9] Perhaps the resolution of this issue may be seen in the theory that situationally lonely people, that is, people who attribute their feelings to unstable causes, have higher expectations that their loneliness will change, whereas chronically lonely people tend to attribute their condition to stable causes and therefore exhibit little hope for change and tend toward apathy.[10]

Obviously there are different degrees and types of loneliness. *Existential loneliness* is that which we all feel at times due to changes such as moving away from friends and familiar places. *Chronic loneliness* is persistent and may contribute to delinquency in adolescents or depression in adults. *Characterological loneliness* stems from character types that tend to steer individuals into risk situations which lead to loneliness. Finally there is *ontological loneliness*, the feeling that one is cut off from ultimate reality. One depressed and lonely patient remarked: "God isn't there anymore." That is the kind of loneliness that was felt by the Ancient Mariner: "So lonely, 'twas that God Himself / Scarce seemed there to be."[11]

The Pervasiveness of Loneliness

Loneliness is a widespread affliction. Yet its prevalence is difficult to quantify. Robert Weiss cites a survey of a "reasonable valid sample of Americans" in which one-fourth of those interviewed declared that they had experienced the pain of loneliness in the past few weeks.[12] Other surveys cited by Weiss indicate that women rather than men are more likely to report personal loneliness, that there is a higher percentage of loneliness among the unmarried, that those who have lost their loved ones by divorce, death, or desertion report a high percentage of loneliness. Surveys also show that the poor are especially likely to be lonely.[13]

Loneliness is no respecter of racial, class, or cultural lines. Every age group is vulnerable. Surveys have shown, however, that it is a myth that old people as a group are particularly prone to loneliness. According to

---

[9]Fromm-Reichmann, "Loneliness," pp. 1-15.

[10]L. A. Peplau and Daniel Perlman, "Toward a Social Psychological Theory of Loneliness," *Love and Attraction: Proceedings of an International Conference*, eds. M. Cook and G. Wilson (Oxford, England, 1979).

[11]Coleridge, *The Ancient Mariner*, VII:599-600.

[12]Weiss, *Loneliness*, p. 1.

[13]Ibid., pp. 1-26.

the research, people in their late sixties, seventies, and eighties are less lonely than younger adults. Indeed, some studies show that loneliness is more prevalent and intense during adolescence.[14]

Every social and vocational group has its lonely individuals. There are the divorced who may suffer deep loneliness—along with a profound sense of rejection—which may be more severe than the loneliness of the single or widowed. Often the single, widowed, or divorced woman finds her social relations limited to other women. For those who have been accustomed to a man as a "significant other" in their lives, this can be a trying experience. The working woman in the big city may find the impersonal and aggressive situation to be exceedingly lonely. The same can be said of unattached males.

Soldiers are among the loneliest of people. I once visited a huge military base and asked a chaplain what was the most serious problem of the soldiers. I anticipated one of the following issues: drinking, gambling, or A.W.O.L. But he replied in one word: "Loneliness." Other institutionalized persons tend to feel the pangs of loneliness. These can be particularly acute among the sick in hospitals, the elderly, shut-ins, and prisoners.

Students in colleges and universities away from home for the first time may become terribly homesick and lonely. Some campuses are so impersonal that a student may go all day to classes without a conversation with someone else. A female student in a prestigious college met her classes, went to the library to study, then back to her apartment. No one had spoken to her nor had she spoken to anyone else that day. Not until she spoke to her cat did she discover she had laryngitis! Foreign students are especially vulnerable to loneliness because they are in unfamiliar surroundings, often with language barriers as well as cultural ones that hamper relationships.

Phillip Shaver and Carin Rubenstein, social psychologists at New York University, have conducted numerous surveys of adults in six American cities. They found that loneliness varies with the time of day and year. Winter, one survey shows, is the loneliest time for people without strong family ties.[15] People also fear to be alone on Friday night. This is especially true of adolescents and young adults. According to

---

[14]Zick Rubin, "Seeking a Cure for Loneliness," *Psychology Today* 13:4 (October 1979): 89.

[15]*What It Means to Be Lonely* (New York: Delacorte Press, 1974).

Shaver and Rubenstein, this is no mystery, for our culture tells us that to be alone on a Friday night is to experience fear, rejection, and loneliness.[16] Often the fear of being alone at any time may motivate youth into unrealistic relationships such as the drug cult, the religious cult, or an unwise marriage.

Sources of Loneliness

Causative factors in loneliness are personal, social, physical, and metaphysical. William Sadler, Jr., refers to sources of loneliness in terms of dimensions. The *interpersonal dimension* relates to one person missing another in death or divorce. *Social dimension* identifies the feeling of being cut off from a group which provides a sense of self-worth and meaning. The *cultural dimension* is the result of separation from a traditional way of life such as experienced by immigrants. The *cosmic dimension* refers to an experience in which the individual feels out of touch with the ultimate source of life and meaning. Some often feel cut off from participating in religious sacraments due to divorce and feel the pain of being shut out of the church and the Kingdom of God. Sadler also refers to the *psychological dimension* of loneliness. It is a feeling of separation from self, of being stymied in the process of self-actualization.[17]

Lack of love in the home also may be a major factor in the loneliness of children. Parents are being replaced by the television set and by peer groups. A million children are running away every year in the United States to join communes or other lonely juveniles. Drugs and sex become escape mechanisms from a sense of aloneness. Religious cults become havens of fellowship and action under authoritarian figures. Some youths desire friendship so strongly they are willing to pay for it. A physician's son in a suburban community paid another lad to be his friend. When he was rejected, the friend-seeker committed suicide.

There are lonely children in both public and private schools. Steve, a shy seventh-grader, turned in his original cinquain poem which his teacher had assigned. It read:

Boy
Thoughtful, lonely.

---

[16]Ibid.

[17]"The Causes of Loneliness," *Science Digest* 78 (July 1975): 58-66.

Reads, listens, thinks,
Wanting to cry out for someone to be his friend.
Man.

Instead of putting his name on his paper, Steve merely put a zero on it. "I'm nuthin'," he explained. He had been in numerous special institutions periodically. His mother admitted she kept him sporadically only because of the monthly check for Aid to Families with Dependent Children she was entitled to on his behalf.

Loneliness may stem from the symbolization of oneself by the evaluations of those one considers most worthwhile. Thomas Wolfe's experience poignantly presents this phenomenon:

> I think I learned about being alone when I was a child about eight years old and I think I have known about it ever since. People, I think, mean well by children but are often cruel because of something insensitive or cruel in their own natures which they cannot help. It is not a good thing, however, for older people to tell a little child that he is selfish, unnatural and inferior . . . because a child is small and helpless and has no defense, although he is no worse than other children, and in fact is as full of affection, love, and good will as anyone could be, he may in time come to believe the things which are told him about himself, and that is when he begins to live alone and wants to be alone and if possible to get far, far away from the people who have told him how much better they are than he is. I can truthfully and sincerely say that I have no bitterness and nothing but pity for anyone who ever did that, but I can also say that the habit of loneliness, once formed, grows on a man from year to year and he wanders across the face of the earth and has no home and is an exile, and he is never able to break out of the prison of his own loneliness again, no matter how much he wants to.[18]

It is evident that the roots of loneliness may be grounded in early childhood from the image one perceives of himself as reflected by others.

[18]Elizabeth Nowell, ed., *The Letters of Thomas Wolfe* (New York: Charles Scribner's Sons, 1956), pp. 370-71.

Retirement from a job or position may trigger the onset of loneliness for some individuals. For the "workaholic," retirement can be extremely unsettling, resulting in depression and even premature death. This is due to the fact that the person is cut off from companionship with comrades on the job, a place to go and to work, and a structured routine to keep him or her active in purposeful activity.

Moving away from the homeplace or town may produce loneliness. Uprooting oneself from friends, kin, and familiar community agencies and services is especially difficult for the elderly who have lived most of their lives in a community where social ties are strong. Young people, when they move, are wrenched from their friends in close-knit groups. The ripping away from the familiar and predictable can leave "raveled edges" as physically painful as exposed nerve endings.

One may be in a crowd and be lonely. David Reisman has brought socio-logical factors to bear on the study of loneliness. He stresses conform-ist tendencies, the desire to fit in, to lose oneself in the group.[19] Mere physical proximity does not insure relational interaction.

Edgar Allan Poe's "The Man of the Crowd" portrays man's craving for the company of others. This is a vivid and dramatic description of the desire to regain contact with other human beings. A "decrepit old man" craves the crowd in London. He relaxes until the crowd thins out and then rushes to another crowded street. The narrator, who has followed the old man for twenty-four hours, grows weary, and stops, and con-cludes: "This old man is the type and genuis of deep crime; he refuses to be alone."[20] (Poe suggests that crime arises from the inability to be alone.)

Some Medical Consequences of Loneliness

There is now enough convincing evidence to link loneliness to disease and premature death. Lynch's research documents in much detail the view that human companionship affects the heart and that there is "reflected in our hearts a biological basis for our need for loving human relationships, which we fail to fulfill at our peril."[21] Symptoms of loneli-ness, he notes, are depression, anxiety, migraine headaches, ulcers, and

---

[19]David Reisman, *The Lonely Crowd* (New Haven, CT: Yale University Press, 1961).

[20]*Great Tales of Edgar Allan Poe* (New York: Simon and Schuster, 1940), pp. 319-29.

[21]Lynch, *The Broken Heart*, p. 14.

hypertension.[22] Physicians have an ethical responsibility to interpret to their patients the medical consequences of loneliness.

Singles, widows, and divorcees experience premature death at a rate anywhere from two to ten times higher than individuals who live with others.[23] Apparently heart disease is linked to loneliness. The coronary death rate among widows aged twenty-five to thirty-four is five times that of married women.[24] The death rate due to hypertension between the ages of twenty-five to fifty-five for nonwhite, nonmarried males is almost double that of married nonwhite males.[25]

Lynch discovered that the state of Nevada with its high singles population, divorce rate, and mobility has a higher death rate from heart disease than neighboring Utah, with its Mormon tradition of family solidarity. He also notes that his fellow Irish have a higher coronary death rate than their countrymen back in Ireland who have a more closely knit culture.[26]

Similar studies show that strong social ties help people live longer. A nine-year study of almost 7,000 Californians reveals that people with few social relationships were two to four and one-half times more likely to die during the nine year period. Begun in 1965, the survey of Alameda County residents indicated that socially isolated men of all ages were about two and one-half times more likely to die during the study than their counterparts with strong social ties. And women between the ages of thirty and forty-nine were almost four times higher risks if they lacked strong social links.[27]

Loneliness may result in a poor life-style and premature death. According to a Surgeon General's report of 1976, fifty percent of the people who died that year died due to poor life-styles (in terms of excessive eating, drinking, smoking, overwork, and a lack of exercise).[28]

---

[22]James F. Lynch, "Warning: Living Alone May Be Dangerous to Your Health," *U.S. News and World Report*, 30 June 1980, p. 48.

[23]Ibid., pp. 4-8, 34.

[24]Lynch, *The Broken Heart*, pp. 239-40.

[25]Ibid.

[26]Ibid., p. 245.

[27]Richard Saltus, *The Louisville Times*, 10 December 1977, p. 1.

[28]Norton-Children's Hospitals *Newsletter* 4:10 (October 1980): 1.

But studies show that those who die living alone die of the same diseases that kill people in general.[29]

Management of Loneliness

According to the Old Testament, the first thing God said was that it is not good for man to be alone (Genesis 2:18). Even Paradise with animals, trees, fruits, and exotic things was not adequate to meet Adam's need for another human companion. So He created Eve, a "helper fit for him." Man is a social being and cannot be healthy and happy wholly alone.

One of the first steps toward the solution of a problem is an understanding of it. Loneliness is the pain of being alone, the feeling of being separated, cut off from some meaningful relationship. Some degree of loneliness is the inevitable experience of everyone for this affliction is no respecter or persons. One may be alone and not lonely. Loneliness is the sense of being alone coupled with despair over one's aloneness. But how to cope with loneliness? Withdrawal into isolation is no solution. It only intensifies loneliness.

The "independent person," totally self-sufficient, as promoted by the media, is a myth. You can only find out who you are in relation to other persons. Every Robinson Crusoe needs his man Friday; and every Lone Ranger, his Tonto. Thoreau's Walden epitomizes the myth of individualism and self-sufficienty in America. But, interestingly, Thoreau's cabin was only one mile from his mother's house where he went to see her almost every day; and he often ate meals with the Emersons and had numerous visitors at Walden.[30]

Substituting chemicals for companions is not an adequate answer either. And pseudoscientific, merchandised remedies have no real therapeutic value. Too often these nostrums only make the merchants rich and leave the customer lonelier than ever. Such negative ways of coping with loneliness should be avoided.

Even as a physician has an ethical responsibility to attempt to restore an optimum healthy balance for a patient, so should the physician seek to provide adequate strategies for combating loneliness. Such strategies may include prescriptions for person-to-person relationships and/or group identification. Other positive steps in coping with loneliness may

---

[29]Saltus, *The Louisville Times*, 10 December 1977, p. 1.

[30]George Satran, "Notes on Loneliness," *Journal of the American Academy of Psychoanalysis* 6:3 (1978): 290-91.

include dialogue, strengthening of family ties, recovering the role of the physician as a resocializer of patients, individual initiative, and turning loneliness into solitude and sociality.

Dialogue with another person or persons is essential to both interpersonal interaction and as an antidote to loneliness. At the age of nine my oldest son saw his mother dying. As a result, it became extremely difficult for him to verbalize feelings. For years I was unable to communicate with him in depth about anything. After his return from the war in Vietnam I confessed to him that I knew that he had been a lonely person for a long time and that I had been insensitive to his needs and too ignorant to know how to converse with him. For the first time we began to carry on a dialogue in depth. When we parted, he said with a smile, "At least now we can talk." His loneliness began to dissipate.

Lynch thinks of dialogue as the elixir of life, and characterizes it as reciprocal sharing, a spontaneous and lively process.[31] He notes that dialogue is fragile and can be interrupted by the loss of a loved one, by divorce or by death, and when children leave home. Such disruptions often are followed by significant increases in illness and death. But dialogue can also deteriorate slowly and subtly to the point where one can become trapped in lonely situations. It can happen in all human relations: in marriage, between parents and children, within the extended family, and among friends.[32]

Mechanical surrogate "parents" or "friends" (television, movies, or other gadgets) cannot meet the need for human companionship. The robot and the computer cannot meet the "need-love" of children or adults because human responses cannot be programmed. There is simply no substitute for the I-Thou encounter in dialogue.

Group identity may be helpful in coping with loneliness. One of the significant discoveries in psychiatry during World War II was that those soldiers who had strong links to groups or participated in a "buddy system" were healthier and less likely to have mental and emotional disorders.[33]

Among the well-known groups aiding the lonely are Alcoholics Anonymous (AA), Parents Without Partners (PWP), Make Today Count, Compassionate Friends, and the USO. These are not merchants of

---

[31]Lynch, *The Broken Heart*, pp. 215-19.

[32]Ibid., pp. 221-31.

[33]Ibid., ch. 7.

loneliness. Rather they are voluntary associations to provide the individual with support and to improve his or her self-image. It is true that at best these provide supplementary relationships characterized by some unrelatedness to the real world of work relations and routine social relations. There is also a danger of persons becoming dependent upon the group. But the values of new friends, activities, and relief from isolation far outweigh the tendency on the part of some to become dependent on the group relationship. Another alternative is that the lonely may participate in study groups dealing with their problems, such as "Seminars for the Separated."

Sometimes a solution to loneliness can be as simple as securing a pet. Those who cannot afford a pet may feed the pigeons, ducks, or fish in the public parks. (While this may appear to be an oversimplification, such activity does provide a pseudosocial involvement where the lonely can move beyond self-absorption.) Millions of singles and lonely couples have pets which are considered an integral part of the family. Because there are so many lonely people in America owning pets, the animal business is a multibillion dollar industry. More money is spent on dog and cat food than on baby food in this country. Research on coronary-care patients who leave the hospital and live alone reveals that those who had pets survived at a higher rate than those without them.[34]

Physicians in past generations contributed to the alleviation of the lonely patient by making house calls. Just the presence of the physician was a healing force. I advocate the recovery of the house-call doctor. Making house calls would better acquaint the physician with his patient, the family, and the patient's socioeconomic status. All of these factors are involved in the effective treatment of the total person. Of course, few doctors are going to volunteer for this kind of ministry. So it is suggested that one year of the physician's residency be devoted to seeing patients in their homes. Tuition—part or all of it—of the medical student could be paid for from tax funds with the stipulation that he or she would devote five years to house-call medical practice. Or the physician could voluntarily devote part of his retirement years to this sort of medical service.

Another way to help lonely patients is to encourage them to take the initiative in coping with their loneliness. One patient I visited in the hospital had just received a large bouquet. I noted on the card that it was

---

[34]Lynch, "Living Alone May Be Dangerous," p. 48.

from "A Secret Admirer." When I teased her a bit, she confessed that no one, not even her pastor, had been to see her, that she was very lonely, and that she had personally called the florist for the flowers. This was her way of coping with loneliness. She fantasized that someone really cared for her. Other patients and staff remarked to her about the lovely flowers, which had indeed served as a catalyst to initiate interaction with other persons.

The churches have a significant role to play in the resolution of loneliness. Regular church attendance is therapeutic and a means of coping with isolation and loneliness. George Comstock and Kay Partridge of the School of Hygiene and Public Health, Johns Hopkins University, did a thorough case-control study in Washington County, Maryland, and discovered a correlation between frequent church attendance and health. It was discovered that men who were frequent (once per week or more) attenders of church services had a coronary mortality rate that was only 60 percent of the rate of those who rarely or never attended church. In women the rate was only 50 percent.[35]

Going to church fulfills to some degree the need for human contact. Just being in church makes people feel like they are part of a community and this tends to reduce loneliness.[36] Shaking hands with the pastor, rabbi, or priest, and with members of the congregation can be therapeutic. Wholesome human contact is always healing.

C. David Jenkins has set forth an abundance of data indicating that anxiety, stress, life change, and other psychological and sociological factors may be risk factors for coronary disease. In *The New England Journal of Medicine*, he cites with a commendation the research of Comstock and Partridge on church attendance and health.[37]

We conclude that man has a biological, psychological, and sociological basis for human interaction. He craves the fellowship of others, and to be alone may result in emotional and physical illness. More research is needed in order to more precisely define and to deal with loneliness. As Frieda Fromm-Reichmann notes: "Aloneness, isolation, loneliness in cultural groups, self-imposed loneliness, compulsory solitude, and real

---

[35]"Church Attendance and Health," *Journal of Chronic Diseases* 25 (1972): 669.

[36]Lynch, *The Broken Heart*, p. 203.

[37]"Recent Evidence Supporting Psychologic and Social Risk Factors for Coronary, *"The New England Journal of Medicine*, Part 1: (29 April 1976): 987-94; Part 2: (6 May 1976): 1033.

loneliness are thrown into one terminological basket."[38] The causes of loneliness need to be clarified and realistic coping mechanisms set forth. Then the therapist can suggest positive possibilities of transforming patients' loneliness into creative solitude and sociality.

The health care professional—it should be noted—needs to recognize his/her own personal areas of loneliness. Developing such a measure of awareness and security will enable the medical person to empathize more effectively with the lonely patient. This will aid in diminishing defensive barriers and thus provide means of more adequate support.

---

[38]"On Loneliness," *Psychoanalysis and Psychotherapy* (Chicago: University of Chicago Press, 1959), p. 325.

CHAPTER 5

The Guilt-Laden Patient:
Types and Therapies

"Guilt," declares Edward Stein, psychologist, "is the peg on which the meaning of 'man' hangs. It is also the peg on which man too often hangs himself."[1] Some of the best minds of every generation have grappled with this issue. Poets (as T. S. Eliot, in *The Wasteland*), novelists (Hawthorne, in *The Scarlet Letter*; Dostoevski, in *Brothers Karamazov*; Kafka, in *The Trial*), philosophers, psychologists, psychiatrists, judges, clergymen and others—professionals and non-professionals—have met head-on the challenge of the problems of human guilt. The significance of the issue of guilt for society was pointed out by psychoanalyst Sigmund Freud in one of his last books. He declared that a sense of guilt is "the most important problem in the development of civilization."[2]

---

[1] *Guilt: Theory and Therapy* (Philadelphia: Westminster Press, 1968), p. 13.

[2] *Civilization and Its Discontents* (New York: W. W. Norton and Co., 1961), p. 81, and chs. 7 and 8.

Guilt is of special interest to physicians and clergymen because it is a form of suffering peculiar to persons. It is the task of both of these professionals to alleviate pain and suffering. Our focus here will be upon the various types of guilt, and upon theories and therapies of guilt.

Terminology and Types of Guilt

Guilt is a complex, multifaceted reality. It is difficult to conceptualize and to explain theoretically because it is related to so many other feelings and factors. Guilt is often intertwined with anxiety, fear, pain, remorse, shame, depression, and deviation from the norms of society. Hence, differential diagnosis is absolutely essential in dealing with mentally and emotionally disturbed persons.

Etymologically the term guilt originally was a payment of a fine for an offense and is derived from the Anglo-Saxon word "gylt" meaning "to pay." It had to do with committing a crime, a breach of conduct, especially such as violates the law and involves a penalty. Thus the dictionary definition of guilt is that of objective guilt. In contrast to this, psychiatric dictionaries define guilt purely from the subjective point of view. Hence, in psychiatry the term seldom refers to *conscious* remorse of doing something wrong, but denotes "a deep underlying subjective guilt which may find expression in obsessive-compulsive reaction or in depression and anxiety as conscious expressions of unconscious guilt feelings."[3]

A more comprehensive concept of guilt will include a description of guilt feeling including the objective and subjective components. Edward Stein provides an analysis of the feeling of guilt when he defines it as "a state of tension or anxiety over internalized aggression (self-hatred) or loss of self-love."[4] He goes on to explain that both internally and outwardly "guilt is anxiety, pain, displeasure, depression, remorse, because of the violation of some internalized values rooted in an emotional relationship."[5]

Guilt also must be seen in its conscious and unconscious, its objective and subjective dimensions. Also, one's concept of guilt must distinguish it from the feeling of shame. Helen Merrell Lynd thinks of guilt as self-reproach, based on internalization of values, notably parental values, in

---

[3]James A. Brussel and George La Fond Cantzlaar, *The Layman's Dictionary of Psychiatry* (New York: Barnes and Nobel, 1967), p. 102.

[4]Stein, *Guilt: Theory and Therapy*, p. 26.

[5]Ibid.

contrast to shame which is based on disapproval coming from outside, from other persons.[6] A similar distinction is made by anthropologist Ruth Benedict who sees guilt as a failure to live up to one's own picture of oneself based on parental values, and shame as reaction to criticism by other people.[7] An examination of the types of guilt will expose the nuances of this phenomenon and provide a fuller understanding of how to cope with it.

Five basic types of guilt may be identified. (1) First, there is *reality-based guilt*. This is sometimes called "real guilt." It is the sort of guilt in which feelings are commensurate with the seriousness of an act and related to the act. This may be called "genuine guilt" because it stems from some violation of human relationships. Or this may be a breaking of a law of God or the state. Tom Oden conceptualizes real guilt as the feeling that "one is inconsistent with oneself."[8] What one has done, in other words, is inconsistent with who one understands himself or herself to be. The intensity of guilt is measured by the depth of the rift between one's image of self and behavior inconsistent with that image.[9] The following case is an example of reality-based guilt.

Jane, twenty-four-year old housewife, was admitted to the psychiatric clinic with the diagnosis of depressive neurosis. Her admission was precipitated by a suicide attempt by medication overdose.

Due to husband-wife conflicts there had been two separations in the past. The husband worked full-time at a store, leaving little time for the patient and their three-year-old daughter. The patient suspected her husband of unfaithfulness. As she became depressed she lost her job as a bookkeeper. She described her feelings: "I feel empty inside like I could collapse and never get up."

Her mental status examination revealed a mood of depression as evidenced by frequent crying spells. But she had no

---

[6]*On Shame and the Search for Identity* (New York: Harcourt, Brace, 1958).

[7]*The Chrysanthemum and the Sword: Patterns of Japanese Culture* (New York: Houghton Mifflin Co., 1934), pp. 222-23.

[8]*Guilt Free* (Nashville: Abingdon, 1980), pp. 64-65.

[9]Ibid.

hallucinations, delusions, no phobias, or flight of ideas. She was coherent. Her personalized response to the proverb, "The grass is always greener in the other fellow's yard," was "I have always heard that a man will run around on his wife, thinking he wants something different."

During her time in the hospital, the patient received individual psychotherapy, expressive therapy, group therapy, and family sessions. In the course of these family sessions, she was encouraged to alter her situation. Though her strongly-held religious views as a Catholic were against divorce, she eventually divorced her husband after exploring alternatives with her therapists.

Currently, as an outpatient, she still has strong guilt feelings about the divorce. "What did I do," she asks, "to cause our marriage to break up?" She is now engaging in self-blame and admits that she took an overdose in order to hurt her husband. She also now feels guilty for hurting people in her attempted suicide, especially her mother and daughter.

In the light of the above case, it is appropriate to note the ethical responsibility of the therapist to refrain from imposing his or her own set of values upon a patient. Utmost respect must be expressed toward the patient's deeply-held moral convictions. For the therapist to ignore such basic beliefs in order to quickly dispose of domestic and other issues shows a lack of professionalism and moral responsibility.

(2) *Neurotic guilt*, or "unrealistic," "irrational," or "false" guilt, is a condition in which feelings are greatly exaggerated beyond the act which the patient confesses, a condition wherein the patient has hoisted aboard too much guilt. Such unrealistic guilt must be distinguished from real guilt. John G. McKenzie makes a clear distinction between the two when he proposes: "Let us keep in mind that unrealistic guilt is subjective; objective guilt refers the guilt-feelings to the actual behavior which has aroused the guilt-feelings. All guilt-feelings are subjective. The criterion of their reality, their normality, is: *Do they refer to a situation which could account for their intensity?*"[10]

Ellen, a sixty-seven-year-old female outpatient, is a victim of abluto-mania, the "Lady Macbeth Syndrome." She constantly washes her hands

---

[10]*Guilt: Its Meaning and Significance* (London: George Allen and Unwin, 1962), p. 23.

and her possessions. She has never married but stays home to care for her widowed mother. She goes out of the house only when necessary and then comes home and bathes. Once she came to the hospital for her medication and psychotherapy with literally raw hands, having washed them in lye to kill the germs. Here is a classic example of compulsive-obsessive behavior. She was diagnosed as having unconscious guilt. These feelings which probably arose from resentment at her mother, and the family dynamics which had trapped her in a seemingly hopeless existence, were repressed by the patient and now found expression in obsessive-compulsive behavior.

(3) *Existential guilt* is a form of guilt that most of us have to some degree. It is related primarily to one's existence rather than one's essence. This type of guilt involves our own finitude, imperfection, and failure in reaching goals. One feels guilty about unfinished projects. You cannot do things that you aspire to do, so you feel guilty about being the sort of person you are. You profess high ideals but never reach them. Then there is old age with the awareness that there is little time left and that those things on the agenda that should have been done are still undone.

(4) *Psychotic guilt* is a feeling of guilt that stems from the delusion that one has committed a wrong. For example, the psychotic patient may feel that he or she has killed someone or robbed a bank, but has actually lived a life free of crime. This type of patient may hear a voice demanding such acts and be convinced that he or she has committed them.

(5) Finally there is *positive guilt*, constructive in contrast to destructive guilt. Normal or constructive guilt is based upon "proportioned valuing," that is, upon the proper prioritizing of finite goals so that they do not become ultimate and idolatrous.[11]

Theories of Guilt

Sigmund Freud was preoccupied with the problem of guilt during much of his adult life.[12] For him, guilt was pathological. Freud maintained that destructive instincts are repressed by the restraints of civilization. In addition, he contended that everyone suffers from a "death instinct," so that hostilities which are not directed outward toward others turn back upon the self in the form of an "intensified masochism" and

---

[11]Oden, *Guilt Free*, p. 74.

[12]Freud, *Civilization and Its Discontents*, especially chs. 7 and 8.

feelings of guilt.[13] When such a death instinct is directed outward it is called "the instinct of destruction, mastery, the will to power."[14] In such a condition death is willed, and the patient dies of a death-wish which is forever in conflict with Eros. The balance of power, that is to say, finally shifts from the aging Eros to the ageless Thanatos which succeeds in doing the individual to death.[15]

For Freud the superego is conscience. He cites two sources of guilt feelings: (1) that arising from the dread of authority, and (2) the dread of the superego. The first compels us to renounce instinctual gratification; the other presses over and above this toward punishment because the prohibited wishes cannot be concealed from the superego.[16] Our moral sense of guilt, then, is the expression of the tension between the ego and the superego.

Even before the death of Freud in 1939, his followers began to depart from his teachings. In the last few decades, a number of psychiatrists not only have departed from Freud, but have rejected some of his basic doctrines. Gregory Zilboorg, American psychiatrist, denies that the superego is the conscience. The conscience is made up of regret, not fear, for having done something wrong. The origin of the superego lies in the ambivalence of fear. Conscience regrets; the superego is angry. Conscience glows with hope when one repents and makes amends. The supergo says: "Wait till next time. There will be something to pay." Guilt, Zilboorg concludes, is more than internalized disapproval of culture and society.[17]

Erich Fromm, eminent psychoanalyst, discovered that "neurosis itself is, in the last analysis, a symptom of moral failure."[18] Likewise Gordon Allport, psychologist, declares that "most of the conflicts that cause damage to mental health . . . have to do with courses of conduct the individual regards as morally obligatory. Whether we call it conscience or

---

[13]Sigmund Freud, "The Economic Problem in Masochism," *Collected Papers* (New York: International Psychoanalytical Press, 1945), 2:258.

[14]Ibid., p. 260.

[15]*An Outline of Psychoanalysis*, trans. by James Strachey (New York: W. W. Norton, 1949).

[16]Freud, *Civilization and Its Discontents*, ch. 7.

[17]*Psychoanalysis and Religion* (London: George Allen and Unwin, 1967).

[18]*Man For Himself* (New York: Rinehart, 1947).

superego, the moral sense is most always involved in any serious conflict."[19]

Among the flood of current "self-help works" is that of Wayne Dyer entitled *Your Erroneous Zones*. Dyer defines guilt as a present moment immobilization about a past event. To put it another way: one experiences guilt when prevented from taking action as a result of previously having behaved in a certain way. Guilt is unhealthy, then, because you are ineffectively using up your energy in the present feeling of guilt, hurt, and depression. Dyer sees two sources of guilt. First, there is "leftover guilt," or emotional reactions carried around from childhood memories which later surface in one's business affairs, leisure activities, and/or sex life. Secondly, there is "self-imposed guilt" by which one is immobilized by recent acts such as breaking a moral code.

As for specific sources of guilt, Dyer calls them "guilt-producing mechanisms." He maintains, for example, that parental "guilt trips" are laid on children. Children in turn engender guilt feelings in their parents. Also there is husband-wife related guilt. Manipulation is achieved by such statements as: "If you loved me . . . ," and "Don't forget what you did in 1965." Beyond this there is institutionally inspired guilt, such as that imposed via prisons, churches, and schools.[20]

Therapies for Guilt

Unresolved guilt can be destructive to the self. Even at the unconscious level guilt may manifest itself in terms of self-sabotaging results. Numerous therapies exist for treating the guilt-laden patient. Two general methods are used: (1) the desensitizing of judgmental attitudes toward one's behavior; and (2) the dissolution of guilt through confession, forgiveness, and restitution. A popular approach to guilt is to help the patient reduce the level of guilt feeling by lowering his or her moral standards which have been violated, or by modifiying superego pressures, at least to the point where non-attainment can be tolerated.

For Freud, as we have seen, guilt is dissolved in the rational self-consciousness fostered by therapy. Guilt is the repression of one's lower nature caused by a person's being overcontrolled by moral constraints. Hence, Freud sought to get his patients to relax their too severe self-discipline. This does not mean, of course, that Freud was not a moral

[19]*The Individual and His Religion* (New York: Avon, 1950), p. 86.

[20]*Your Erroneous Zones* (New York: Avon, 1976).

person. In his clinical writings, he reveals how he restrained his disgust for the sexually deviant, "scoundrels," and the "good for nothing" so as not to react with moral condemnation to a patient.[21] Freud counseled his patients to relax their self-expectations in relation to the conventional morality and piety of the time. He believed that overly strict expectations resulted in neurotic guilt. Yet Freud was not an amoralist advocating a profligate life-style. Freud did argue, however, that although traditional religion had served mankind well, shepherding it through its infancy, that with the maturing of minds religion must die of its own disenchantment. This includes Christianity which was nothing more than a painful "historical residue." Now, Freud contended, religious motives for right behavior could safely be replaced by secular ones.[22]

Another therapy used to desensitize severe judgmental attitudes toward one's own behavior is by utilizing drugs. Drug therapy is actually a behavioral technique for the treatment of patients with high levels of guilt. Two British researchers have recommended this approach as an alternative to psychoanalysis. It is based on the application of the principle of behavioral modification. The method is rather simple. Intravenous methohexitone sodium in a two and one-half percent solution is injected slowly as a sub-anaesthetic dosage. During this process, the patient is asked to visualize situations that have made him or her feel guilt. When the patient is completely relaxed, hyperarousal due either to excitement or anxiety is inhibited when evoked by the stimulus.[23] In this desensitizing method, according to Friedman and Ashley, there should be two or three assessment interviews. Generally three treatment sessions each week for four weeks produce lasting behavior modification in the majority of patients. When the maladaptive behavior ends, treatment is terminated.[24]

One of the basic flaws of such desensitizing therapy as that described above is that the sense of guilt is not dissolved; it is only minimized so that the patient can cope with it. Paul Tournier holds that psychoanalysis

---

[21]Robert Holt, "Freud's Impact on Modern Morality," *Hastings Center Report* 10:2 (1980): 38-45.

[22]*The Future of an Illusion* (New York: Liveright Publishing Corporation, 1949), pp. 76-77.

[23]"A New Technique for the Treatment of Guilt," *British Journal of Psychiatry* 130 (1977):586-91.

[24]Ibid.

does not eliminate guilt, but only shifts it.[25] In a similar vein, John McKenzie declares that the one cure for the burden of real guilt is forgiveness; this the psychotherapist cannot give. Indeed, he may dissipate unrealistic guilt feelings due to wrong concepts. But he cannot displace guilt feelings that stem from real guilt. Says McKenzie: "He cannot offer forgiveness which alone can lift the burden. He cannot offer a meaning to life, no affection for which the patient is seeking."[26] "Real guilt," as Andra Angyal observes, is an emotional reaction to having acted against someone or something with which one is genuinely identified, for example, in an act of disloyalty. "Real guilt" is also an offense against one's own integrity. Or it can be perceived as a betrayal of someone or something one loves. Such internal conflicts require forgiveness and cannot be psychotherapized away. In this sense, "real guilt," as it directs a person toward a sense of error, thereby prompting the need for forgiveness and reconciliation, can be seen as a positive and integrating force in the personality and not necessarily a destructive one.

There is also a growing conviction among psychotherapists that psychoanalysis does not adequately deal with the ethical dimension of guilt. O. Hobart Mowrer, an American psychologist, became disenchanted with some of the basic teachings of psychoanalysis. He repudiated many of the existing psychiatric assertions about pathological guilt. He was especially concerned about "ethical neutrality" in psychoanalysis. He emphasizes *real* guilt, sin, and values. He holds that both Freud and Protestantism have defected from code morality. The neurotic person does not suffer from a severe superego, but from a lack of moral courage to do what his better judgment dictates is right and best. If the patient suffers from guilt which is a genuine reaction to real offenses and transgressions, then the role of therapy is to get the guilt-laden patient to recognize his evil ways, conform to accepted moral standards, and to sin no more.[27] Hence, Mowrer seeks to reinvoke realistic moral challenges in psychotherapy similar to that of William Glasser who lays emphasis upon the acceptance of reality and responsibility.[28]

---

[25]*Guilt and Grace* (New York: Harper and Row, 1962), p. 128.

[26]McKenzie, *Guilt: Its Meaning*, p. 147.

[27]*The Crisis in Psychiatry and Religion* (New York: D. Van Nostrand Co., 1961).

[28]*Reality Therapy: A New Approach to Psychiatry* (New York: Harper and Row, 1975).

Likewise, Abraham Maslow has forcefully described the need for a healthy system of moral norms. "The state of being without a system of values," he says, "is psychopathogenic. . . . The human being needs a framework of values, a philosophy of life, a religion or religion-surrogate to live by, in about the same sense that he needs sunlight, calcium or love."[29] Both subjective and objective guilt involves responsibility for something or someone. John G. McKenzie observes that we cannot be responsible for some things such as an environment we cannot change; but we do have instinctive tendencies that make us subject to praise or blame. How we direct these tendencies in relation to cultural influence and personal insight is the determining factor. Ethical guilt includes more than just duty; there are indeed guilty emotions (such as malice), evil sentiments, and wrong motives. To the extent one allows these to govern behavior, to that extent he is guilty of evil.[30]

This brings us to the second major method of guilt therapy, namely, the dissolution of guilt. It is the aim of both psychiatry and religion to make individuals whole persons. But there can be no wholeness without the resolution of real guilt. The religious approach to the problem of guilt involves a process which includes a sense of guilt, confession, repentance, restitution, and reconciliation. This whole approach to real guilt must be seen in terms of theological therapy.

From the biblical perspective, guilt is described in the Old Testament basically in terms of moral failure. The Hebrew term *asham* refers to the concepts of fault, blame, sin, and trespass. Guilt is the violation of God's laws and man's rights (Genesis 26:10; 42:21; Numbers 5:6-8; Proverbs 30:10). Two terms in the New Testament further describe the experience of guilt. *Enochos* is the Greek word meaning to be guilty of something, to be "caught in" some wrong doing (Matthew 26:66; 1 Corinthians 11:27). *Ptaisei* (from an old verb "to trip") means losing one's balance, tripping and falling (James 2:10). Guilt in this sense, then, is falling below one's potential and God's expectations. According to the Genesis account, Adam and Eve *fell* from their state of innocence when they disobeyed God, whereupon they felt guilty and hid themselves from the presence of God. Guilt can be viewed, then, as closely related to moral conscience *(suneidesis)*. It can be a good, bad, or weak conscience (1

[29]*Toward a Psychology of Being* (New York: D. Van Nostrand Co., 1962), p. 192.
[30]McKenzie, *Guilt: Its Meaning*, ch. 4.

Timothy 1:19; 1 Corinthians 8:7-10). It is a faculty which reminds us, by triggering feelings of guilt, that we have done wrong.

An acknowledgement of guilt is the first step toward forgiveness and wholeness. Confession is the second step in grappling with guilt. The Judeo-Christian tradition is replete with acts of confession of guilt. David, the king of Israel, confessed his acts of adultery and murder as sins against God. Though forgiven, David had to pay a heavy price for his sins (2 Samuel 12:1-14). The Hebrew people confessed collective guilt before God (Nehemiah 9:3); a penitent described his experience of confession and forgiveness from "the guilt of my sin" (Psalm 32:1-5); and the Prodigal Son confessed his sin against heaven as well as his father and thus received forgiveness (Luke 15:11-32).

A third step toward forgiveness and wholeness is that of contrition or repentance. Contrition is sincere sorrow for wrong doing and a desire to make amends. This is called restitution, the act of restoring to the rightful owner something that has been taken away or lost. It is compensating for a damage done to a person, animal, or thing. After an encounter with Jesus, Zacchaeus offered to restore fourfold any goods he had acquired by fraud (Luke 19:1-9), evidence of a genuine conversion. Obviously, reparation under certain circumstances is not always a wise course of action. Of the Twelve Steps of Alcoholics Anonymous, two have to do specifically with restitution. The alcoholic is to make a list of the individuals he or she has harmed and be willing to make amends to them all. But step nine declares amends are to be made except where to do so would cause more injury to them or others. This is a sound principle.

Unfortunately there is no clear teaching in Protestantism on penance or restitution. The guilty want to know what they can do to atone for guilt. Restitution is the practical side of the answer.

A patient had divorced her husband and entered a business career. She felt guilty about the divorce, about an illicit sexual alliance with a business partner, and about neglecting her three children. She became depressed and came for help to the psychiatric clinic. Her therapist recognized that the woman had a religious problem; she kept saying that she was afraid God was punishing her. The therapist was able to convince her that God forgives, but still she didn't feel forgiven. She felt the need to atone for her wrong behavior. So the therapist suggested that she "go and sin no more" with her business partner, try to develop specific plans for being a more effective mother to the children, and seek to banish her anger toward her former husband. She agreed to this strategy, proceeded to do "penance" in these respects, and appeared to achieve a better quality of life.

Reconciliation is the final stage in the process of dissolving guilt. To reconcile is to reestablish a lost friendship. To use Martin Buber's categories, it is a restoration of the I-Thou from the I-It relationship. A basic component is that of *acceptance*. The therapist must accept the patient as a whole person. It is an affirmation of the other who has a low self-image and engages in self-blame. Again, the forgiven must accept the forgiveness of the other. And the forgiver accepts the one who has violated his or her love or trust, including the anguish and guilt of the other. To extend one's love to the other is to bring the whole person back into a mutual relationship of respect and responsibility.

Acceptance is not a new therapeutic concept. The Early Church practiced it. The apostle Paul admonished: "Accept one another as God for Christ's sake has accepted you" (Romans 15:7, author's translation). Acceptance is a strong Greek term demanding the acceptance of the *total* person—race, color, and social status included. God's acceptance of persons is the theological basis of the ethical requirement of our acceptance of others who seek forgiveness. When the guilt-laden patient *accepts his or her acceptance* of self, of others, and of God, there is the realization of reconciliation.[31]

Forgiveness is involved in the act of reconciliation of the offender and the offended. The offense becomes no longer an alienating factor. There is atonement (at-one-ment). In relation to God, forgiveness is personal, complete, and final. The Psalmist prayed:

> Have mercy on me, O God, according to
>   thy steadfast love;
> According to thy abundant mercy blot
>   out my transgressions.
> Wash me thoroughly from my iniquity,
>   and cleanse me from my sin! (Psalm 51:1-2, RSV).

---

[31]*The Courage To Be* (New Haven: Yale University Press, 1952), p. 164.

The term "blot out" is from the Hebrew *machaha*, "to erase," as from a tablet or blackboard; it means to check off, to expunge, to efface guilt and sin. The Psalmist pleaded to be "washed" of his iniquity. By *kabas*, to wash, he means to wash out his guilt so that he cannot see it. And the word *taber*, to cleanse, means to remove his guilt so that God cannot see it.[32]

Can the psychotherapist as well as the clergy hear confession and witness such a liberation from the bondage of guilt? Paul Tournier thinks so, and so do I. The lay psychotherapist can do so on the basis of the doctrine of the priesthood of all believers. Tournier discovered this truth when he himself began wholeheartedly to practice confession. As a result he became aware of a "spiritual ministry." Many who have come to him for counseling have found freedom as a result of confessing their faults and guilts.[33]

Tournier believes that confession has religious as well as psychological significance. It is impossible, he thinks, to dissociate the physical, psychological, and religious dimensions of life. Every physician, with or without specializing in psychotherapy, "if he understands what is human and likes contact with human beings, may suddenly find himself promoted to a confessor's priesthood without having sought it."[34]

Catholics, of course, would not be satisfied with a layman's absolution. But the therapist can encourage the patient to go to the church for confession. Likewise people of other religions may be referred to proper places, persons, or deities to whom confession should be made. A Protestant doctor can, when the patient confesses guilt and sin, point to God's promises in the Bible regarding forgiveness. A theological consultant or a chaplain in the psychiatric clinic can often serve effectively with the psychiatrist and work toward the breaking of the bonds of guilt.

---

[32]I am indebted to J. J. Owens, Th.D., noted Semitic scholar, Southern Baptist Seminary, Louisville, KY, for these insights on Psalm 51:1.

[33]Tournier, *Guilt and Grace*, p. 202.

[34]Ibid., p. 204.

CHAPTER 6

The Homosexual:
Some Theories and Therapies

Homosexuals are coming "out of the closets" all across the country. They are pressuring for their basic rights as citizens in a democratic society. Traditionally, they have been denied certain rights, such as free sexual expression, equal employment opportunities, and even membership in churches. Indeed, homosexuals have been considered criminals and have received heavy sentences, up to life in prison, for practicing homosexualism.

Are these persons mentally and emotionally ill as is argued by some psychiatrists? Is homosexuality a disease, or a way of life? Is it sin or sickness? Can it be cured? To get at these and other questions, I shall describe some of the empirical data in terms of categories and etiologies (causes).

Homosexuality: Some Empirical Perspectives

Homosexuality is a term derived from the Greek word *homos* meaning one and the same, and is defined generally as sexual attraction between persons, male or female, of the same sex. *Homosexualism* is the practice of homosexuality. This definition of homosexuality is inadequate because it does not distinguish between the degrees and types of homosexuality. Differential diagnosis is, therefore, essential to understanding the homosexual. On a heterosexual continuum rating scale from zero to six, individuals can be classified according to their overt behavior, their psychic response, or both. Between the exclusive heterosexual and the exclusive homosexual there are different degrees of homosexuality.[1]

Among the categories of homosexuality are:

• *transient homosexuality* which occurs in the preadolescent period and may stem from curiosity or experimentation

• *substitutive or situational homosexuality* where there is an absence of the opposite sex such as during periods of prison confinement

• *pseudohomosexuality* or *latent hososexuality* in which the person has either a conscious or unconscious impulse toward homosexual behavior but does not overtly act on it

• *episodic homoseuxality* in which the person engages in both homosexual and heterosexual activities

• *exclusive homosexuality* in which the person consistently engages in homosexual activity[2]

• *ego-dystonic homosexuality* which involves a persistent desire to acquire or increase heterosexual arousal and a sustained pattern of overt homosexual arousal that is undesired and a source of distress.[3]

Stereotypical thinking about the homosexual is fallacious. There is no such person as a "typical" homosexual. For example, the popular notion that all male homosexuals are effeminate has no foundation in fact. According to C. A. Tripp, effeminacy is relatively rare in homosexuality.[4] The fact is that masculinity is highly valued in gay society. Other myths about homosexuality—such as that all are brilliant, artistic, child molest-

---

[1]Wardell Pomeroy, "Homosexuality," in Ralph Weltge, ed., *The Same Sex: An Appraisal of Homosexuality* (Philadelphia/Boston: Pilgrim Press, 1979), pp. 7-8.

[2]See Lionel Ovesey, *Homosexuality and Pseudohomosexuality* (New York: Science House, 1969), p. 31.

[3]*Diagnostic and Statistical Manual of Mental Disorders*, 3rd ed. (Washington, DC: American Psychiatric Association, 1980), p. 281.

[4]*The Homosexual Matrix* (New York: McGraw-Hill Book Co., 1975), p. 9.

ers, and/or promiscuous—have long since been exploded, but they linger on.[5]

Homoerotic practices vary in the sex act. Mutual masturbation, oral-genital contacts, and anal intercourse are common practices among male homosexuals. Places of homoerotic encounters are gay bars, coffee shops, autos, public restrooms ("gay tearooms"), parks, parking lots, offices, churches, homes of friends. These are cruising grounds where liaisons frequently take place. Promiscuity is frequent among male homosexuals. They apparently are more often concerned with a "one-night stand" and a succession of partners than settling down to a permanent relationship. Obviously, such sexual encounters are impersonal and primarily for sexual satisfaction.[6]

Homosexuality is a complex phenomenon with multiple causation. More than sixty-five etiological factors have been reported in male homosexuality alone.[7] Among the major theories of causation are: (1) the constitutional or biological-genetic or hormonal factors theory;[8] (2) Freud's view of underlying castration anxiety and unresolved Oedipal situations; and (3) the pathogenic family theory which is the most prevalent theory today. It is often held that a parental constellation consisting of a detached, hostile father, and a possessive, dominating, overprotective, and "demasculizing" mother is the most significant factor in the production of the male homosexual. But the fact that many heterosexuals have similar family backgrounds and do not go on to become homosexuals suggests that this theory is inadequate in and of

---

[5]Kimball Jones, *Toward An Understanding of the Homosexual* (New York: Association Press, 1966), p. 27; Evelyn Hooker, "Homosexuality," in Elizabeth S. and William H. Genne, eds., *Foundations for Chrisitian Family Policy* (New York: National Council of Churches, 1961), pp. 168-69; Gordon Westwood, *Society and the Homosexual* (New York: E. P. Dutton and Co.; London: Gollancz, 1952), pp. 132-33; Albert Ellis, "Homosexuality and Creativity," *Journal of Clinical Psychology* 4:4 (October 1959): 377.

[6]See Laird Humphreys, *The Tearoom Trade: Impersonal Sex in Public Places* (Chicago: Aldrine, 1970), pp. 60-68.

[7]*Changing Homosexuality in the Male* (New York: McGraw-Hill, 1970), pp. 34-35.

[8]See S. James, et al., "Significance of Androgen Levels in the Aetiology and Treatment of Homosexuality," *Psychology of Medicine* 7:3 (August 1977): 427-29; R. C. Friendman, et al., "Hormones and Sexual Orientation in Men," *American Journal of Psychiatry* 134:5 (March 1977): 571-72; B. Zuger, "Monozygotic Twins Discordant for Homosexuality: Report of a Pair and Significance of the Phenomenon," *Comparative Psychiatry* 17:5 (September-October 1976): 661-69.

itself. The fact is that homosexuality is multidetermined by biological, psychodynamic, sociocultural, and situational factors.[9]

My own thinking on the matter of etiology is that homosexuality is largely learned or acquired. At birth, as Freud observes, human beings have the capacity for both heterosexual and homosexual orientation. There is really no inborn tendency toward either sexual life style. Homosexuality develops later in life as the sexual drive is conditioned by one's environment. "We may speak," says Wainwright Churchill, "of a *tendency* toward heterosexuality and/or a *tendency* toward homosexuality. But this tendency is *acquired* and is a product of learning rather than a part of the individual's biological inheritance."[10]

Is homosexuality an illness? Students of the issue are divided in their opinions. Psychiatrist Edmund Bergler, after thirty years of treating homosexuals, concludes that "they are sick people."[11] He thinks that it is a neurotic disease with ten unconscious factors involved. A male homosexual: (1) is "an exquisite injustice collector, and consequently a psychic masochist"; (2) is a fugitive from women; (3) is perpetually on the prowl, "cruising" (seeking a short-term partner); (4) more than the heterosexual, specializes in one-night stands; (5) uses the husband-wife camouflage or smoke screen so as to appear as a heterosexual; (6) has a megalomaniacal outlook on life—is convinced of his superiority over others; (7) has gay hiliarity which is a thin pseudophoric camouflage; (8) has inner guilt arising from the perversion which denotes infantile sex encountered in an adult; (9) exhibits irrational jealousy; and (10) is unreliable and uses unsavory short cuts and detours of conspiracy.[12]

Martin Hoffman, who represents the position of many students of homosexuality, declares that in itself homosexuality does not necessarily indicate mental illness. Psychiatric studies, he observes, are based on samples that are not necessarily representative of the homophile community. Hence, he concludes: "Homosexuals seen in psychiatric treatment are no more representative of homosexuals in the general

---

[9]Alfred M. Freedman, et al., *Comprehensive Textbook of Psychiatry*, vol. 2, 2nd ed. (Baltimore: Williams and Wilkins Co., 1975), pp. 1510-20.

[10]Wainwright Churchill, *Homosexual Behavior Among Males* (Englewood Cliffs, NJ: Prentice-Hall, 1967), p. 105.

[11]*Homosexuality: Disease or Way of Life* (New York: Collier Books, 1967), p. 105.

[12]Ibid., pp. 13-25.

population than are Jews seen in psychiatric treatment representative of all Jews."[13]

In 1974, the American Psychiatric Association substituted a new definition and category for homosexuality and called it "sexual orientation disturbance." This category is for persons whose sexual interests are directed primarily toward people of the same sex and who are either disturbed by, in conflict with, or wish to change their sexual orientation. This diagnostic category is distinguished from homosexuality, which, in itself, does not necessarily constitute a psychiatric disorder.

In 1980, the American Psychiatric Association adopted a new diagnostic category for homosexuality called ego-dystonic homosexuality. The diagnostic criteria appear in the new DSM (Diagnostic and Statistical Manual of Mental Disorders, third edition, 1980) and are summarized here as follows: The person under study "complains that heterosexual arousal is persistently absent or weak and significantly interferes with initiating or maintaining wanted heterosexual relationships"; and there prevails "a sustained pattern of homosexual arousal that the individual explicitly states has been unwanted and a persistent source of distress." Hence, homosexuality that is ego-syntonic is not classified as a mental disorder.[14]

There does appear to be a higher incidence of neurotic personality disorder among homosexuals than among heterosexuals. But given a society like ours in which being a homosexual is likely to be subjected to ridicule, contempt, rejection, and even punishment by the state, it would be a miracle if most homophile persons did not suffer emotional and mental illness.[15] Yet many homosexuals function honorably and responsibly, often in positions of highest trust, and live well-adjusted lives with a minimum of distress because of their sexual preferences.

Homosexuality is the most common sexual deviation and occurs in most countries and among all socioeconomic classes. In 1948, Alfred Kinsey and associates reported that no less than thirty-seven percent of the male population had some homosexual experience between adoles-

[13]The Gay World: Male Homosexuality and the Social Creation of Evil (New York: Basic Books, 1968), p. 157.

[14]Diagnostic and Statistical Manual of Mental Disorders, p. 282.

[15]Freedman, Comprehensive Textbook of Psychiatry, pp. 1517-18.

cence and old age.[16] But these figures are faulty because they include individuals with only one homosexual experience. Kinsey states that about four percent of all white males are exclusively homosexual throughout their lives.[17] Female incidence of homosexual experience was reported as less than half of that for males.[18]

Irving Bieber estimates that there are two million homosexuals in America.[19] Daniel Webster Cory, a homosexual writer, declares that there are more homosexuals than there are people with heart disease or cancer.[20] Lewis Williams concludes that there are at least fifteen million homosexuals in this country and that they make up the nation's second largest minority group.[21] The fact is that it is impossible to determine with any degree of accuracy the number of homophiles in America. The social stigma and resulting persecution related to homosexuality make it exceedingly difficult and at times even dangerous to "come out of the closet." The figures presented above may represent only the tip of the iceberg.

For centuries the homosexual has been the subject of harassment, discrimination, persecution, and punishment by the state. Penalties for homosexual behavior in the United States range all the way from one year to life in prison in some states. In thirty-one states, sex between consenting adults of the same sex is a crime. (Sodomy laws have been repealed in nineteen states: California, Colorado, Connecticut, Delaware, Hawaii, Illinois, Indiana, Iowa, Maine, Nebraska, New Hampshire, New Mexico, North Dakota, Ohio, Oregon, South Dakota, Washington, West Virginia, and Wyoming.) No consistency prevails in the application by judges, juries, and policemen of laws against homosexuals. Some homosexual law reform has been initiated, notably by the Wolfenden Commit-

[16]*Sexual Behavior in the Human Male* (Philadelphia: William B. Saunders Co., 1948), p. 623.

[17]Ibid., p. 651.

[18]*Sexual Behavior of the Female* (Philadelphia: William B. Saunders Co., 1953), pp. 474-75.

[19]"Speaking Frankly on a Once Taboo Subject," *The New York Times Magazine*, 23 August 1964, p. 75.

[20]"Homosexuality," in Albert Ellis and Albert Abarbanel, eds., *The Encyclopedia of Sexual Behavior* (New York: Hawthorne Books, 1961), 1:490.

[21]"Walls of Ice: Theology and Social Policy," in W. Dwight Oberholtzer, ed., *Is Gay Good?: Ethics, Theology and Homosexuality* (Philadelphia: Westminster Press, 1971), p. 172.

tee in England, the American Law Institute in America, the American Psychiatric Association, and the National Institute of Mental Health. All such reform movements call for decriminalization of private sexual behavior between consenting adults.[22]

Homosexuality in the Context of Theology

Homosexuality must be viewed not only from the standpoint of empirical data but also from the perspective of biblical revelation. For centuries the attitude of the church has been that of contempt rather than compassion, rejection rather than redemption. As we shall see, the church has overacted to homosexualism and made it the "abominable sin."

Biblical Perspectives on Homosexuality. Genesis 19:4-11 is most often cited as a major teaching about homosexuality. In this passage, the men of Sodom demanded that Lot turn over to them his two guests that they might "know them" (verse 5). By some it is argued that this phrase means to "get acquainted" and that the central teaching of the passage is not the sin of sodomy but of inhospitality.[23] But the phrase "to know" *(yada)* means carnal knowledge. The same word is used in verse 8 where Lot offers his virgin daughters to the men of Sodom in lieu of his guests.[24] Judges 19 tells a similar story. In this passage (verse 22) there can be no doubt that *yada* means homosexual coitus because the "base fellows" of the town demanded intercourse with the male guest.

It is true that both of these stories deal with intended homosexual rape and not homosexual relationships between consenting adults. Even so, this does not mean that homosexual behavior between consenting adults was condoned. Indeed, Leviticus 18:22 and 20:13 clearly teaches that homosexual relations between consenting Israelite males were considered wrong because such relations violate the male and female order of creation.

---

[22]*The Wolfenden Report: Report of the Committee on Homosexual Offences and Prostitution* (London: Stern and Day, 1963), paragraph 18.

[23]John McNeill, *The Church and the Homosexual* (Kansas City: Sheed Andrews and McMeel, 1976), pp. 42-50; D. S. Bailey, *Homosexuality and the Western Tradition* (New York: Longmans, 1955), pp. 1-28.

[24]William Gesenius, *A Hebrew and English Lexicon of the Old Testament* (Boston: Crocker and Brewster, 1872), p. 380.

In the New Testament Jesus never mentions homosexuality. In Romans 1:26-27, Paul speaks of heterosexuals, both men and women, who have "exchanged natural relations" for "unnatural relations." Here homosexuality is placed within the context of idolatry. The people had become confused about the identity of God (verse 23) which resulted in a confusion about their own identity. Hence, they perverted natural human sexuality into homosexuality (verses 25-27).

In 1 Corinthians 6:9-10, Paul includes homosexuals in a catalogue of the kinds of persons whose behavior is not in conformity to the will of God. *Malakoi* and *arsenokoitai* are in the list of those who shall not inherit the kingdom of God. *Malakoi* has the meaning of "soft" with reference to persons and things. The King James Version puts it "effeminate." Walter Bauer notes that the terms relate to persons who are soft and effeminate, especially catamites, "men and boys who allow themselves to be misused homosexually."[25] While there may be some doubt about the specific meaning of *malakoi* in the above passage, there can be none about the meaning of *arsenokoitai*. It is translated "homosexuals" in the Revised Standard Version, "pervert" in Phillips Modern English Version, and "homosexual perverts" in the Today's English Version. Thayer's *Greek-English Lexicon of the New Testament* defines it as "one who lies with a male as with a female, sodomite." Bauer agrees that the term means sodomite.[26] Sodomy is also condemned in 1 Timothy 1:10 and Jude 7.

Some writers have sought to "read out" homosexual behavior between consenting adults in all of the above passages. In each case it is said that homosexuality is condemned in terms of rape or male prostitution rather than sex between consenting male adults. At any rate there is not a single passage in the Bible that supports consensual sex relations between male adults. The fact remains that there is a general condemnation of homosexualism (overt act) in both the Old and New Testaments.

Theologizing About Homosexuality. The Church Fathers, the Reformers (Luther and Calvin), and other Christian theologians through the centuries have condemned homosexual behavior.[27] In the Catholic

[25]*A Greek-English Lexicon of the New Testament*, trans. by William Arndt and Wilbur Gingrich (Chicago: University of Chicago Press, 1957), p. 489.

[26]Ibid., p. 109.

[27]John Calvin, *The Epistle of Paul the Apostle to the Romans and to the Thessalonians*, trans. by Ross Mackenzie (Grand Rapids: Wm. B. Erdmans Publishing Co., 1961), p. 36.

tradition, Aquinas reasons that, since sex organs must be used for pro-creation, sodomy and bestiality are wrong because nature's rule of hetero-sexuality is violated.[28]

In the tradition of the Fathers and Reformers, Karl Barth rejects the homosexual orientation and relates it, as does Paul (Romans 1:27-28), to idolatry.[29] In Barth's opinion, homosexuality is "the physical, psychologi-cal and social sickness—perversion, decadence and decay which can emerge when man refuses to admit the validity of the divine com-mand."[30] Barth notes that Romans, chapter 1, reveals how homosexual-ity becomes inhumanity without the elements of fellow-humanity, the latter being rooted in the togetherness of man and woman. So inhuman-ity results from the idea of a masculinity free from woman or a femininity free from man. In essence, for Barth, homosexuality is willful and deliberate sin, a refusal to hear the divine command. But he adds that the doctor, the pastor trained in psychotherapy, the legislator, and the judge must know God's grace as well as his demand and put forth their best efforts for the protection of youth.[31]

Helmut Thielicke criticizes Barth for his lack of charity and human understanding, and makes a plea for law reform relating to homosexual-ity. He favors placing it on a plane along with disease and suffering as contrary to God's will in creation. Moreover, the homosexual must be willing to undergo treatment so as to be brought back into the order of creation. Thielicke almost sanctions homosexual love, but ends up by counseling sublimation.[32]

A statement by some English Quakers in 1963 fully sanctions the homosexual life-style. It calls upon Christians to re-evaluate their tradi-tional attitudes toward homosexuality. Homosexual acts, it is claimed, are neutral.[33] Homosexuality, therefore, can be used for either good or evil and should be no more deplored than "left-handedness." It is the nature

---

[28]*Summa Theologia*, part 2, section 2, pp. 152-54.

[29]*The Epistle to the Romans*, trans. by E. C. Hoskyns (London: Oxford University Press, 1950), pp. 42-54.

[30]*Church Dogmatics*, vol. III/4 (Edinburgh: T. and T. Clark, 1961), p. 166.

[31]Ibid.

[32]*The Ethics of Sex*, trans. by John Doberstein (New York: Harper and Row, 1964), pp. 269-92.

[33]Alastair Heron, et al., *Towards A Quaker View of Sex* (London: The Society of Friends, 1963), p. 26.

and quality of the relationship that matters for homosexual affection can be as selfless as heterosexual affection and is not morally worse.[34]

The Homosexual as Patient

Can homosexuality be "cured?" Here again the specialists have a divergence of opinion. Gay liberationists are irritated and angered at the suggestion of prevention, much less cure or change. Almost all students of the problem agree that unless the homosexual really wants to change, very little can be done toward effecting change. When homosexuals do seek to change their sexual patterns, they do so because they have difficulty in attracting partners, problems of depression, self-realization, and some form of disorder or neurosis. If treatment fails to effect change, some psychiatrists attempt to help homosexuals to accept their sexual orientation without shame and to function as responsible persons.[35]

Therapy for Homosexuality. A number of therapies are used for homosexuality. These can be identified within three categories: the *hetero-strategy*, the *homo-strategy*, and the *sublimation strategy*.

The *hetero-strategy* includes: (1) intensive psychotherapy or psychoanalysis which have helped some who have wanted to change to heterosexual orientation; (2) drug therapy for anxiety and depression stemming from the homosexual status in an unfriendly society; (3) group therapy may be helpful to some; and (4) behavioral modification. Negative or adversive conditioning may be applied. Homoerotic pictures, for example, may be shown accompanied by an injection in the patient of apomorphone to produce an unpleasant feeling and vomiting. Or a painful electric prod may be tried as an aversion technique. A positive modification technique may consist of what is popularly called "Playboy Therapy." This involves graded masturbation exercises at home, enabling the male patient to ejaculate while looking at erotically stimulating pictures of females.

The *homo-strategy* acknowledges the client's lack of desire to change and seeks to help him or her adjust to the homophile lifestyle. An effort is made to alleviate feelings of disgust, anxiety, and fear, and to find a support system for the patient within the gay community. Gay social, political, and religious groups, especially a gay church, can aid the homosexual.

---

[34]Ibid., p. 36.

[35]Freedman, *Comprehensive Textbook of Psychiatry*, p. 1519.

The *sublimation strategy* as a therapeutic approach involves absti-
nence from sexual activity with another person. This strategy calls for
discipline and long-term outpatient treatment.[36]

The Homosexual Patient and Physician Confidentiality. One of the
problematic ethical issues arising out of the physician-homosexual
patient relationship is that of confidentiality. Harvey Kuschner relates
the following example:

> David, the oldest of three children, was the son of a well-
> to-do manufacturer. David's father valued physical prow-
> ess and athletic accomplishments, areas in which David
> showed little interest. When David was twelve or thirteen
> years old, conflicts with his father resulted in almost nightly
> arguments. It was evident that David's father had become
> concerned about David's mannerisms and considered them to
> be effeminate.
>
> David's schoolwork deteriorated considerably and he
> became withdrawn. His father decided to send him to a mil-
> itary school, but he remained there for only six months. By this
> time, David had told his parents that he was a homosexual,
> had engaged in, and was engaging in homosexual practices.
> He came home and completed his high school studies, but did
> not go on to college and continued to live at home.
>
> He was treated for gonorrhea, asthma, and infectious
> hepatitis. At the age of twenty-one, to gain exemption from
> the draft, his physician attested to the fact that he was a
> homosexual.
>
> Five years later, Joan visited her family physician for a
> premarital serological exam. The physician was the same
> physician who had treated David. Joan was twenty-four years
> old and had been under this physician's care since the age of
> fourteen. A close and warm relationship had developed
> between the physician and Joan's family, and it was normal,
> then, for the physician to ask about her fiance. When he did, he
> learned that she was about to marry David. She had known

[36]*The Hastings Center Report* 7:2 (April 1977): 15.

him only briefly, but well enough, she felt, to be certain about her choice. Nothing more was said at the time.

David and Joan were married shortly thereafter and lived together for a period of six months. The marriage was annulled on the basis of nonconsummation. David told Joan that he was homosexually oriented, and she learned as well that not only did they share a physician but also that the physician was aware of David's homosexuality. She subsequently suffered a depression as a result of this experience and was angry that her physician had remained silent about David. She felt that she could have been spared this horrible episode in her life—that it was her physician's duty to inform her. His failure to do so was an act of negligence resulting in deep emotional scars.

To whom did the physician owe primary allegiance? Do the interests of one patient prevail over the requirements of confidentiality surrounding another's case?[37]

Should the rule of confidentiality be honored even under these circumstances? What is the responsibility of the doctor to each patient? Both appear to have implicit trust and confidence in their physician. He indeed has the obligation under the Hippocratic oath to "do no harm." Is it harmful—or merely cowardly—to maintain a discreet silence? Are there ever circumstances which justify disclosure of privileged information?

Summary

Homosexuality is a fact of life. As to its etiology we have only theories. Prognosis for experienced homosexuals is not too encouraging. Yet some psychiatrists claim that from twenty to fifty percent have a chance for change. Intensive psychotherapy can be effective in a change of sex orientation if the patient has a strong motivation to change. If not, the therapist can help the homophile to accept his or her sexual preference for one of their own kind and live within a disapproving society. With the emergence of the gay movement, the homosexual is gaining more rights as a citizen. As for the church, a positive role can be played by recognizing that its teaching calls for the redemption, not the destruction, of all persons made in the *imago Dei*.

---

[37]Judd Marmor, "Homosexuality," in Freedman, *Comprehensive Textbook of Psychiatry*, p. 1519.

CHAPTER 7

In Vitro Fertilization
and Surrogate Motherhood:
Some Ethical Reflections

In the book of Genesis, it is reported that God appeared to Abraham, who was one hundred years old, and announced that the patriarch and his wife Sarah, who was ninety, would at last have a son, an heir. Upon hearing this, Abraham "fell on his face," beat the ground, and laughed in disbelief (Genesis 17:17). Sarah also laughed when she heard the news. This is understandable because she was no longer sexually active and was obviously too old to bear a child (Genesis 18:11-12). Yet Sarah did indeed conceive, and a son was born to the elderly couple. This conception can be considered a miracle of divine grace.

Currently—without divine intervention—human reproduction can be achieved in several ways. In addition to the natural method of coitus, the major alternative means of reproduction are artificial insemination, surrogate motherhood, in vitro (literally, "in glass," that is, in a culture dish) fertilization, and the possibility of cloning. In this study the focus will be upon human in vitro fertilization and surrogate parenting, and on some ethical issues related thereto.

Human in Vitro Fertilization

Half a century ago Aldous Huxley, in his futuristic novel, *Brave New World*, predicted the production of "test-tube babies" within the next six hundred years A.F. (After Ford). So far as conception is concerned, this has already been accomplished. In 1978, doctors Patrick Steptoe and Robert Edwards in England announced the birth of Louise Joy Brown, the first baby to be conceived in a test tube or glass dish.

The process of producing a "test-tube baby" is called *human in vitro* (in glass) *fertilization* or reproduction. In the initial step of the process, the physician uses a laparoscope, a surgical tool with lens and light, to search for a mature egg or ovum in the female's ovary. Using a suction needle, the egg is then transferred to a culture dish (not a test tube) containing life supporting nutrients and sperm. A single sperm penetrates the egg, fertilizing it. After two or three days, the fertilized egg reaches the eight-cell stage. This developing egg is then returned to the uterus through the cervix by means of a plastic tube (cannula). The uterus has been prepared to receive it by administered hormones. Some days later, the growing fertilized egg attaches itself to the uterine wall and grows into a fetus.

The impact of the birth of the laboratory-conceived Louise Joy Brown was immediate. Doctors Steptoe and Edwards received hundreds of requests from women all over the world for aid in conception. In 1979, when it was learned that the East Virginia Medical College in Norfolk planned a fertility clinic for in vitro reproduction, more than 2,500 women in the United States and many parts of the world applied for test-tube babies. Many of them, like Louise Joy Brown's mother, had blocked fallopian tubes and could not produce babies by means of the conventional method. Estimated costs for in vitro fertilization per patient range from $1,500 to $4,000.[1] It is estimated that, of the couples of childbearing age, approximately ten percent are infertile. About sixty percent of this infertility is related to female difficulties; and, of these, the biggest problem is related to blockage of the fallopian tubes.[2]

---

[1]"Test-tube Clinic," *Newsweek*, 5 March 1979, p. 102.

[2]John L. Marlow, "British Birth Poses Many Problems to Society," *U.S. News and World Report*, 7 August 1978, p. 24.

When the birth of the first test-tube baby was announced, a heated debate about the ethicality of such a procedure was touched off. Theologians, philosophers, physicians, scientists, and nonprofessionals are currently engaged in arguments pro and con this new mode of human reproduction.[3]

There is the ethical question as to the spiritual and moral status of the early embryo. Some, especially the Catholic church and pro-life proponents, hold that human life and ensoulment occur at conception. With this presupposition, it is tantamount to murder to destroy fertilized eggs at any stage of development: as a zygote (one-celled, that begins to divide after twenty four to thirty six hours), a morula ("little mulberry," sixteen-celled), or a mature blastocyst (approximately 110 cells, and ready to be implanted in the uterus).[4] But many others (including scientists) reject the view that prenatal life at any stage is human in the sense of being "a person" with the right to life.[5]

Joseph Fletcher and others have sought to distinguish the human from the nonhuman. Twenty tentative criteria of humanhood are set forth by Fletcher.[6] Out of these twenty criteria, he later selected four which he thinks are valid. First, there is the *neocortical function* which is the key to humanhood. It is the basic human trait, the sine qua non, upon which all the other three criteria of personhood hinge: *self-consciousness, relational ability,* and *happiness.*[7] Obviously the application of Fletcher's criteria of humanhood to the early cell formations after conception—the zygote, blastocyst, and embryo—would indicate that they are nonhuman. This means that in vitro human fertilization could be accomplished without the possibility of destroying human beings.

---

[3]For an excellent analysis of the literature on the subject see Leroy Walters, "Human In Vitro Fertilization: A Review of the Ethical Literature," in *The Hastings Center Report* 9:4 (1979): 23-43.

[4]For a description of these developments see Ruth Fowler and R. G. Edwards, "The Genetics of Early Human Development," in Arthur Steinberg and Alexander Bearn, eds., *Progress in Medical Genetics* (New York: Greene and Stratton, 1973), p. 78.

[5]For example, Joseph Fletcher, "In Vitro Fertilization of Human Ova and Blastocyst Transfer," *Journal of Reproductive Medicine* 11:5 (November 1972): 198.

[6]"Indicators of Humanhood: A Tentative Profile of Man," *The Hastings Center Report* 2 (November 1972): 1-4.

[7]"Four Indicators of Humanhood—The Inquiry Matures," *The Hastings Center Report* 4 (December 1974): 4-7.

Sissela Bok declares that we should reject humanhood as a criterion for judging in vitro fertilization. She holds that the criterion should be based upon our reason for the protection of life: to guard against suffering and harm to the victim, to the agent, to the family, to friends, and to society as a whole. This, Bok thinks, does not apply to the "earliest cell formation soon after conception."[8] But she hastens to add limits to abortion at the quickening and viable stages. Before quickening, Bok suggests, abortion could be by request. While at the few-cell stage there is the *potential* of humanhood, Bok thinks that the killing of an embryo cannot be equated with murder, since most of the reasons we protect lives are absent. However, as the growth of the embryo progresses, it becomes more human and has more rights and need for protection. At any rate, Bok's view of personhood allows for in vitro human fertilization.

Some ethical issues are related to experimentation. Many lab-fertilized eggs are lost or destroyed. But approximately fifty percent of embryos are lost during the first two weeks of the gestation period of normal human reproduction in the female body. Thus it is difficult to see how the death of early embryos in vitro can be considered death of human beings.[9] How can all spontaneously aborted and in vitro embryos be human beings with souls? No one has yet been able to pinpoint with adequate data the stage of ensoulment and personhood of the embryo. Yet the embryo is clearly a potential human being. Does it have the same rights at conception as does the mother? I think not. But it begins to accumulate rights as it develops toward becoming a human being.

Some argue that in vitro fertilization is not God's plan of reproduction. Procreation is divorced from the monogamic "one flesh" relationship of husband and wife. The only legitimate mode of reproducing, it is argued, is coital. But where this is impossible in some females, are they to be deprived of children of their own when the means for conception and full-term delivery are available? Some churchmen equate the "means" with adultery, but how can this be so when there is no sex act, no passion, no lust? The argument that medical laboratory-produced babies dehumanizes the natural process and depersonalizes the parents is not valid. Rationally planned parenthood is most human and natural. Children

---

[8]"Ethical Problems of Abortion," *The Hastings Center Studies* 2:1 (January 1974): 42.

[9]See George V. Lobo, *Current Problems in Medical Ethics: A Comprehensive Guide to Ethical Problems in Medical Practice* (Allahabad, India: St. Paul Publications, 1974), pp. 103-106.

produced ectogenesis, beginning outside, truly wanted and rationally chosen, are most likely to be loved and cared for.

There is the fear that in vitro reproduction may become a commercial enterprise. Opponents envision ova or egg banks for commercial purposes. "Baby farms" are envisioned where infants of various types could be mass-produced, perhaps even to serve the state. Alan Toffler, the futurist, predicts "babytoriums" where one can shop for the kind of baby one desires.[10] There would be, it is feared, the possibility of females engaging in the business of using their bodies as "hot houses" for prenatal adoption. Donation of fertilized eggs is seen as possible to gestational or surrogate mothers. For example, if a woman could not have a baby, or if having one would interfere with her career, she could "rent a womb."

Surrogate Motherhood

Surrogate, substitute, motherhood is already a fact of life.[11] Fees for assuming the role of surrogate mother may be modest or can run into thousands of dollars. Is it not worth the cost for a woman who deeply desires a child? Those who attempt to adopt children find the process long and discouraging. Besides, many persons prefer children of their own genetic lineage or, at least, of the spouse's. The following letter illustrates this fact:

Dear Professor Barnette:

My husband and I read your article on Biomedical Reproduction. We have been trying to adopt a child, but have not been able to do so. I cannot have a baby. Is there a way my husband's sperm can be injected into the womb of another woman? Do you have embryos to put in a rented womb? If this can be done, how much would it cost? I hope that you can answer my questions as I have wanted a child so long.

Sincerely,

(Mrs. John Doe)

What is the legal status of the child borne by a surrogate mother? Is there not a danger of incest?[12] How about the legal vulnerability of the

---

[10]*Future Shock* (New York: Random House, 1970).

[11]"Pregnancy by Proxy," *Newsweek*, 7 July 1980, p. 72.

[12]*Newsweek*, 22 September 1975, p. 87.

doctor who may accidentally destroy a fertilized egg? A federal jury awarded a woman $50,000 for emotional damages resulting from her doctor's deliberately destroying the test tube containing the embryo that was to be transferred to her womb.[13]

The surrogate-mother method of achieving parenthood is a spin-off from the long-practiced artificial insemination procedure which has produced approximately 20,000 babies annually in this country. Surrogate mothering involves the implanting of the prospective father's sperm into the surrogate mother's uterus; the egg thus fertilized she carries to full term in a proxy capacity for the would-be mother. At birth the surrogate relinquishes all claim to the child, is paid for her services as prescribed by contract, and the formerly childless couple has an offspring fathered by the husband.

Some of the ethical issues confronting the medical professional in regard to this matter would include the following:

• Is surrogate motherhood a form of prostitution or adultery? No, because the intent of the persons involved is pro-family as opposed to lust or deliberate sexual exploitation.

• Should lesbians or homosexual males have the right to this means of securing children? No. This would create problems for the child who needs a father-mother pattern.

• Will the practice of surrogate motherhood destroy the institution of marriage? No, the method is too costly.

• Should the children conceived by surrogate motherhood be told of their conception? Disclosure would serve no positive purpose and the chance of "intermarriage risk" in minimal.

Other relevant issues have legal implications. For instance, what happens if:

• the baby is born badly malformed?
• the surrogate mother decides to have an abortion?
• the couple divorces or one partner dies during the pregnancy?
• the surrogate mother dies?
• the surrogate mother decides to keep the baby?
• the birth is multiple?
• the state law prohibits payment to a surrogate mother? (A recent opinion by the attorney general of Kentucky declared surrogate mother-

---

[13]See "Test-tube Bereavement," *Newsweek*, 31 July 1978, p. 70; and *The Louisville Times*, 19 August 1978, p. A2.

ing illegal. This, however, is only advisory, and does not have the force of the law.)

In summary, it is my belief that surrogate motherhood is a viable option for couples with a fertility difficulty. But those involved should be mature, responsible, legally married people who view with utmost seriousness their participation in the life-giving process. Only in this respect can surrogate motherhood be ethically justified.

We have looked briefly at some of the ethical issues in lab human fertilization. Females lacking the capacity to have natural-born children can now produce them through in vitro fertilization. As in the case of every discovery, that which is discovered may be used for good or ill. I conclude that in vitro fertilization and surrogate parenting places man in co-creativity with God and that this is ethically acceptable, providing this procedure is used for the good of those involved.

Experimentation must proceed in a manner in keeping with the principle of medical ethics: "First, do no harm." Positively stated, research must be done in harmony with the ethic of agape-love which means to will the well-being of the other. To support this principle, legal safety guidelines must be established now.

The Attitude of the Churches
toward in Vitro Fertilization and Surrogate Parenting

The attitude of the churches and their theologians toward new forms of fertilization varies greatly. Both Roman Catholics and conservatives tend to see it as a deviation from the natural, God-ordained way of reproduction. Catholics put these two forms of fertilization in the same class with artificial insemination and contraception which they condemn. On the other hand there are individuals in many faiths, including Catholics, who welcome such developments. Arthur Dych, professor of ethics at Harvard University, holds that we must "improve on nature and try to perfect the process because we value the life that God gave us."[14]

With reference to the churches vis-à-vis scientific research in general and lab reproduction in particular, I suggest the following:

(1) *The churches should maintain an attitude of openness toward scientific research in the field of the new medicine.* Through the centuries theologians of the churches have tended to resist scientific research and

---

[14]*U.S. News and World Report*, 7 August 1978, p. 23.

progress, often with absurd justifications. Theological opposition has been strong against new discoveries and techniques. Until modern times some of the leading church theologians, including Augustine and Tertullian, opposed anatomical studies. Surgery was forbidden on the basis of the doctrine of the resurrection in the Pauline teachings. Mutilation of the body by surgery, it was thought, might hinder bodily resurrection. Throughout the Middle Ages the belief prevailed that there was in man an imponderable, incorruptible, incombustible bone which was the necessary nucleus of the resurrected body. For over a thousand years surgery was considered dishonorable by theologians of the church.

For centuries the church taught that man had one rib less on one side than on the other. This idea was based on the biblical story that when God created Eve, he utilized one of the ribs of Adam. Subsequently, surgeons revealed that man indeed has an equal number of ribs on each side.

Likewise, ecclesiastics and theologians opposed inoculations. In the 1700s, Boyer in France presented inoculations as a preventative of smallpox. For this he was condemned in both France and England. In 1772, the Rev. Edward Massey of England published a sermon entitled "The Dangerous and Sinful Practice of Inoculation." In it he declared that diseases are sent by Providence as punishment for sin and, therefore, to prevent such diseases is a "diabolical operation."[15]

In 1721, Dr. Sabdiel Boylston of Boston inoculated his own son. Ministers and doctors alike condemned him, charging that it was "an encroachment on the prerogatives of Jehovah whose right it is to wound and smite."[16] But two leading ministers of New England, Increase Mather and Cotton Mather, supported inoculation. Because he sheltered another minister who supported inoculation, a lighted grenade was thrown into Cotton Mather's house.

Edward Jenner (1749-1823), English physician, developed vaccination. There was strong opposition among theologians and physicians to vaccinating a human being. A Dr. Mosely wrote a book condemning vaccination and placed on the title page the following words: "Father, forgive them, for they know not what they do."[17]

---

[15]Andrew White, *A History of the Warfare of Science with Theology in Christendom* (New York: D. Appleton and Co., 1896), 2:55-57.

[16]Ibid.

[17]Ibid., p. 58.

In 1847, James Young Simpson, a Scottish physician, advocated the use of the anesthetics in obstetrical cases. His use of chloroform was denounced among clergy as being contrary to Holy Writ which declared that, as part of the curse on women, they were to bring forth children in pain. However, his opponents began to have second thoughts when Simpson noted that God put Adam to sleep when he removed one of his ribs to create Eve.

It should be noted that throughout the Middle Ages there were a few laymen, ecclesiastics, and especially Jews who promoted medical science. But some suffered at the hands of the church. Andreas Vesalius (1514-1564), a Belgian anatomist, one of the first to dissect the human body, made a pilgrimage to the Holy Land (1564) in fulfillment of a condition for the commutation of his death sentence by the Inquisition for desecration of the human body by dissection.

As the new medical techniques proved to be effective in curbing and curing diseases, opposition to them declined. The notion that diseases result from the wrath of God or the malice of Satan was steadily weakened. But even today such views remain. For example, members of certain Dutch religious sects reject vaccination for polio. One father of an ailing child said in a TV interview: "God must decide who is struck down by sickness, not the doctors." Luke 5:31 is cited as a sanction against vaccination: "Those who are well have no need of a physician, but those who are sick."[18]

Generally, churches today more readily accept new technologies in biomedicine. Perhaps this is due to the growth and dissemination of knowledge in the field of science. At any rate, theologians of the churches should stimulate, not stifle, research as long as it conforms to love.

(2) *Few things are more frightening than ignorance in action.* Knowledge is essential in moral decision making and action, especially in the area of biomedicine. In order to make constituents more knowledgeable about scientific research and technological developments, the churches can provide seminars, literature, and lectures.

(3) *The churches can and should provide biblical guidelines for research and action.* It is the role of the churches to provide moral leadership based upon biblical ethics as well as scientific data. Love is the central ethical motif in the Christian faith and it means to will the well-being of the other.

---

[18]*The Louisville Times*, 1 August 1978, p. A4.

(4) *With reference to in vitro reproduction, the church can affirm that there are both good and bad possibilities.* This is true of every new discovery. In my own judgment, there is no basic contradiction between biblical teaching and in vitro fertilization or surrogate parenting, provided the doctors are competent and committed to doing the most loving thing, which is to provide a viable alternative to infertility for couples who cannot conceive in the so-called natural way.

Scientific research will continue at an accelerated rate. A major task of the churches must be to encourage the establishment of moral guidelines for research and to continue in dialogue with the individuals and institutions concerned. Efforts to prevent research would be contrary to the inquiring mind, and to the Scriptures which teach us that we are to test all things and to hold on to that which is good (1 Thessalonians 5:21), and that:

> It is the glory of God to conceal things,
> but the glory of kings is to search things out
> (Proverbs 25:2, RSV).

CHAPTER 8

Genetic Engineering:
Some Ethical Questions

All of us are products of a genetic stream traceable all the way back to Adam. From the beginning of man, genes have carried the genetic code which determines our physical makeup: the color of skin, eyes, and hair, physical size, and so forth. And from the beginning of human beings, the genes have functioned in this way.

Sociobiologists now are telling us that our attitudes and actions (such as selfishness or altruism) are products of the genes and can be traced back to our most primitive ancestors. Altruism, for example, in terms of throwing oneself upon a grenade to shield one's comrades, is not so much a noble act as it is a genetic impulse. Dr. Edward Wilson, a Harvard University entomologist, holds that religion, altruism, and morality all evolved and have roots in the genes. He reasons that language and religion are genetic because they are human and universal.[1]

---

[1] See *On Human Nature* (Cambridge: Harvard University Press, 1978).

Genes, and Goals of Genetic Engineering

The substance of which genes are a part is a long chainlike molecule called deoxyribonucleic acid or DNA. This DNA is the chemical record in which hereditary information is encoded. Genes are molecules of DNA and the basic units of heredity.

Each cell of the human body has forty-six chromosomes which carry the genes that convey hereditary characteristics. The chromosomes are arranged in twenty-three pairs. Of these, twenty-two pairs are autosomes (any of the paired chromosomes other than the X and Y sex chromosomes). One pair of sex chromosomes determines the sex of the individual.

At the time of fertilization the chromosomes from the sperm unite with the chromosomes of the ovum. At that moment the sex of the embryo is determined. The ovum may contribute an X chromosome to the embryo. The sperm may contribute an X or a Y chromosome as its half to join with the chromosome derived from the ovum. Thus, the embryo may have XX in its sex chromosome, in which case a female would develop; or XY in which case a male would develop.

Genetic engineering is the alteration of some aspects of the genetic structure. Goals of this procedure are: (1) to enable people to give birth to a child; (2) to ensure that the child will be normal; and (3) to produce human beings with the finest possible genetic attributes.

The Polluted Genetic Pool

Human genes become defective by mutation and by chromosome aberration, and such defective genes are passed on to one's progeny or offspring. Some geneticists think that the genetic pool in the United States is overly polluted with defective genes. One of the basic reasons is that (by means of modern medicine) people with defective genes have survived and have produced offspring who, in turn, carry genetic defects. For example, insulin has increased the number of people with diabetes who may have produced children with the defective gene or genes.

Prevalence of Genetic Defects. The cells of every individual carry three to ten potentially harmful genes. About one person out of five has a genetic defect which will be passed on to the offspring.[2] Leroy Augenstein estimated that, in 1972, six percent of the births in this country were

---

[2]James B. Nelson, *Human Medicine: Ethical Perspectives on New Medical Issues* (Minneapolis: Augsburg Publishing House, 1973), p. 99.

defective.[3] In the United States, about 250,000 children are born every year with genetic diseases. Four million Americans are born with diabetes. Approximately fifty million Americans have an I.Q. below ninety.[4] Approximately twenty-five percent of our hospital beds are occupied by persons suffering conditions wholly or in part genetically related. About one third of our hospital beds are occupied by mental patients and, of these, possibly eighteen percent are patients with defective genes. Fifteen percent of all cases of true mental retardation are genetic in origin.

Purifying the Genetic Pool. Eugenics is the science concerned with the improvement of hereditary qualities. Four major types of genetic engineering control are used to achieve these qualities. *Negative eugenics* seeks to limit transmission of defective genes through adoption of children and sterilization. *Positive eugenics* uses the techniques of artificial insemination by donor (AID) in cases where the husband carries defective genes. Sperm banks are also used which makes viable sperm available for reproduction.[5] *Gene selection* for test-tube babies and cloning is another method. Finally, there is the method of *genetic structure alteration* by chemical or microsurgical techniques. Rearranging the genetic structure and replacing defective genes with healthy ones could eventually eliminate many hereditary diseases.

Byelorussian scientists are reported to be working at the Hereditary and Medical Genetics Laboratory of the Minsks Medical Institute with the aim to purify the gene pool of the Russians. These scientists claim that the lines on people's palms are coded signals of genes responsible for the formation of a human organism and the key to the mystery of many family diseases. The laboratory has set up a special medical genetics clinic which handles hundreds of patients each year. In addition to treating people suffering from genetic diseases, married couples along with young people considering marriage come for counseling. The counselees are concerned about avoiding passing on hereditary diseases to their children.[6]

---

[3]"Birth Defects," in M. Visscher, ed., *Humanistic Perspectives in Medical Ethics* (London: Pemberton Publishing Co., 1972), p. 207.

[4]Robert Shinsheimer, *Eugenics and Science* 35 (June 1972): 7.

[5]Herman Muller, "Means and Aims in Human Genetic Betterment," in T. M. Sonneborn, ed., *The Control of Human Heredity and Evolution* (New York: Macmillan Co., 1965).

[6]*Soviet Life* 8:227 (August 1975): 48.

Genetic Counseling

Genetic counseling aims at preventing the conception of individuals with serious hereditary diseases and disorders. Genetic data are gathered and the counselor presents the facts to the counselees. Risks of having a genetically defective child are stated and alternatives presented. But the counselee must be the ultimate decision maker regarding the available options.

Prior to the 1960s the method of "medical mathematics" was used to predict the possibilities of genetic defects of an embryo. A careful history of the family of a suspected defective gene carrier was made. The number of defective children in the family and the family tree were noted. Adding up the data, the counselor explained the mathematical probabilities of having a defective child.

In 1955, the technique of amniocentesis was developed whereby nearly 100 genetic disorders can be detected by examining the amniotic fluid of a pregnant woman. The procedure, performed between the 13th and 18th week of pregnancy, consists of penetrating the amniotic sac, usually with a long needle and syringe, and removing amniotic fluid which contains fetal cells. These are analyzed in the laboratory for metabolic or chromosomal defects. If, for example, it is discovered that a woman has a defective fetus, she has the option to abort.

Genetic Screening

Genetic screening is the testing of an individual or a group of persons to determine whether they are carriers of defective genes. Prenatal screening is done by amniocentesis. Postnatal screening refers to testing and detection of genetic defects after birth by a blood sample or by a skin cell test. A new technique for prenatal screening is being developed which is destined to replace amniocentesis. Trophoblastic cells which have broken away from the fetal placenta and entered the mother's blood stream can be tested as early as the fifth week of pregnancy.[7]

Currently, screening tests are made for sickle-cell anemia which occurs in about ten percent of Blacks. The victim has abnormal red blood cells shaped like a crescent or a sickle. Few live beyond forty years of age.

---

[7]Darrell S. English, "Genetic Manipulation: Past, Present, Future," in Nancy and John Ostheimer, eds., *Life or Death: Who Controls?* (New York: Springer Publishing Co., 1976), pp. 35-55.

Some Blacks have objected to sickle-cell screening, labeling it genocide of the Black race.

Tay-Sachs disease afflicts about ten percent of the Jews in this country. It is characterized by progressive degeneration of the cerebral function and death occurs before the age of three. Jews have willingly submitted to screening for the disease.

Phenylketonuria (PKU) is characterized by brain damage and severe retardation due to acid in the urine. In 1972, forty-three states required hospital tests for PKU in all newborn babies.

These and other diseases can be detected by genetic screening. The goals of such screening are to detect genetic diseases at an early stage and to guide those so afflicted to medical help; to detect carriers of genetic diseases so that they can make informed choices about having children; and to alleviate the anxiety of noncarriers of hereditary diseases.

Recombinant Genetics

About five years ago biochemists developed a method for mixing genes from any two organisms and to produce a whole new creature. Sometimes called "gene splicing" or recombinant DNA, the procedure is to take the DNA groupings called "plasmids" and split one from two different organisms and mix them. When mixed they recombine into a hybrid plasmid, bearing some characteristics of both original organisms.

Some possible benefits of gene splicing are: progress against genetic diseases and cancer; new forms of life for growing superwheat and other plants that produce their own fertilizer; and combatting pollution (for example, organisms to eat oil spills).

Human insulin is now possible via DNA. Animal insulin from sheep, pigs, and cows now required daily by one and a half million people in the United States eventually will be replaced by human insulin. Through new techniques of genetic engineering a group of scientists at the City of Hope National Medical Center, and Genetech, Inc. of California are harnessing the gene to make human insulin. Gene splicing is the basic process by which human insulin is produced. Animal insulin is only ninety-eight to ninety-nine percent pure and sometimes has some unpleasant side effects in patients. The new insulin is practically pure. Possibilities for other vital medicines from DNA technology are enormous.[8]

---

[8]"The Miracle of Spliced Genes," Newsweek, 17 March 1980, pp. 62-71.

Some possible dangers of recombinant DNA are: the production of a disease-causing bacterium which resists an agent which normally controls it; the development of creatures which have the power to reproduce themselves and spread throughout the population, upset the delicate ecological balance, and cause new diseases in human beings and plants.

Scientists do make mistakes and accidents can happen. In August 1980, Dr. Samuel Ian Kennedy, virologist at the University of California at San Diego, cloned the wrong virus, but claimed there was no health threat, although the experiment violated the federal rules set up by the National Institute of Health for cloning and DNA research. Dr. Kennedy had cloned the semliki virus which causes fever and headache instead of the sindbis virus which causes skin rash and fever. He was seeking agents to combat the virus when he accidentally cloned the semliki virus. The material is now in storage pending an investigation.[9]

Strong reactions against recombinant genetic experimentation have been expressed. In June 1976, the city council of Cambridge, Massachusetts, learned that Harvard University was planning a new laboratory for recombinant experiments. The council voted a moratorium on all potentially dangerous DNA research, but it was lifted after safe guidelines for experimentation were established.

Despite strong opposition in various parts of the nation to recombinant DNA research, over one hundred institutions and corporations are involved in it. Among these are Harvard, Princeton, Columbia, Indiana University, Miles Laboratories, Eli Lilly, Upjohn, and General Electric.

In 1980, the United States Supreme Court ruled, five to four, that scientists can patent new forms of nonhuman life. The decision grew out of a case filed by General Electric as a result of the discovery by an Indian geneticist Ananda Mohan Chakrabarty in a G.E. laboratory, a virus that may consume oil spills. More than one hundred applications for patents on living organisms are on file at the United States Patent Office and are expected to be approved.[10]

Ethical Reflections on Genetic Engineering

A bundle of ethical issues arise from genetic manipulation. In relation to genetic counseling and screening, who owns the data? Does the doctor

---

[9]*The Courier Journal* (Louisville), 8 August 1980, p. A6.

[10]"Justice," *Newsweek*, 20 June 1980, p. 74.

or the patient own it? Does the counselor have the right to furnish data, for example, on a sickle-cell anemia patient, to an employer or an insurance company? Does society have a right to require genetic screening for carriers of defective genes? Does the state have the right to force carriers of defective genes to refrain from producing genetically defective children? Denmark does this, holding that society's right transcends that of the individual. Marriage licenses are denied in Denmark to persons carrying certain genetic defects until one of the couple has been sterilized.

Ethical questions arise when the genetic counselor informs parents that they are about to have another badly malformed child. Consider the following case. The parents already have one child afflicted with Downs Syndrome. In the light of the fact that the woman has already borne one Downs (formerly called Mongoloid) child which will cost the taxpayers about one-half million dollars because the child is institutionalized, does she have the right to bring another fetus to term? Another Downs child will add to the tax burden. In addition, there will be the trauma for the family of giving birth to another malformed child. The father and siblings again will share in the trauma along with the mother. When the parents asked the genetic counselor what he would do, he refused to answer the question. He declined, as he said, "to play God."

The above case was presented in Grand Rounds at the University of Louisville School of Medicine. The geneticist turned to me and declared that I would talk about the ethical implications of the case. This I did not anticipate, but I had to express my convictions on the matter before that conclave of physicians and staff members. First, I indicated that my guiding ethical principle was *agape* which means to will the well-being of the other. In this case I felt that it would be the most loving thing to abort the fetus and save the mother and the members of the family from the stress and strain of coping with a badly malformed child, and the taxpayer another financial burden. Some disagreed, and that was their right and privilege, but I still hold to my initial thoughts on the ethical issues rising out of the case. Some of the most complex and perplexing problems in contemporary society are in the area of biomedicine, as this case well illustrates.

The Bible does not speak directly to the issues raised by genetic manipulation. However, the God of biblical revelation wills the health of His children. This is a solid principle in Scripture. God desires human beings to be whole persons. When genetic engineering, in the control of competent and caring engineers, is used to improve mankind genetically, socially, and culturally, it is in keeping with God's will of love.

A popular proverb was circulated in ancient Israel: "Our fathers have eaten sour grapes, and the children's teeth are set on edge" (Ezekiel 18:2). The proverb was used by some to blame their failures on heredity and the environment, but the prophet Ezekiel warned his generation that God forbids its use to avoid one's responsibility for one's condition. With our knowledge of heredity today we can no longer resort to this proverb in relation to some of our physical and mental problems. Each one of us can be responsible for our own genes which infect or endow our offspring. We can give our children bad genes as well as a bad environment. We can pass on a blessing or a curse. It is our duty to pass on to our children healthy genes. This responsibility is in harmony with God's will of love, the willing of the well-being of oneself and others.

CHAPTER 9

Communicating with Patients in Extremis

Clear communication is especially important in physician-patient relationships because it plays a significant role in the health of the individual. Francis Bacon observed that "a man were better relate himself to a statua [statue] or picture, than to suffer his thoughts to pass in smother [suppressed]."[1] Repressed feelings, thoughts, or ideas, often result in mental and emotional disorders. Just to know that one is being heard is healing. Stephen Crane describes a person with a tongue of wood who tried to sing. Only one person heard and understood.

> But there was one who heard
> The clip-clapper of this tongue of wood
> And knew what the man
> Wished to sing,
> And with that the singer was content.[2]

---

[1]"Of Friendship" in *The Harvard Classics*, vol. 3 (New York: Collier Press), p. 73.

[2]Stephen Crane, "There Was a Man," *The Collected Poems of Stephen Crane*, ed. by Wilson Follett (New York: Alfred A. Knopf, 1957, p. 95.

Without meaningful communication both the individual and society can become sick and suicidal.

The Concept and Criteria of Communication

Like so many terms today in our radically changing culture, communication has lost some of its meaning from much use and abuse. Lack of communication is used to explain failures in institutions, government, business, and interpersonal relations. One can easily rationalize error or unjust actions by saying that it was all due to "a lack of communication." For example, a certain patient who frequently abuses his wife physically, is the father of a child by his teenage stepdaughter, and is now charged with improper relations with a second stepdaughter, recently declared to me that the problem between him and his wife was "merely the problem of communication."

Conceptualizing Communication. What is communication? The term comes from the Latin *communicare*, "to make common," "to share." It is related to the terms "communion," "commune," and "communism." This includes the ideas of command and commune (to converse intimately). Martin Buber and Karl Jaspers, noted Jewish philosophical theologians, stress the dimension of the commune idea and reject the epistemological doctrine that all true knowledge is gained by objectivity alone. Rather they claim that it comes through "empathy" and intersubjectivity. For them and others these are keystones of communication.[3]

Genuine communication does involve both facticity and empathy. It is the data process which originates in a mind and ends in a mind. The source is the brain; the data is transmitted by the vocal chords, body language, and attitudes. The channel is the air waves and vision; the receiver is the other person's brain.

Communicating clearly is an art. It involves skill in the performance of conveying ideas, facts, and feelings as accurately, comprehensively, and as cogently as possible. The art of communicating is learned by experience, study, observation, and intuition.

Communication can be mentally and emotionally contagious. Psychic and emotional "germs" are conveyed from one person to another. The rebel yell of the Confederates in the War Between the States often demoralized the Yankees. Emotional, manipulative verbal communicat-

---

[3]Martin Buber, *Between Man and Man* (London: Kegan Paul, 1947), pp. 1-30; Karl Jaspers, *Man In The Modern Age* (London: Routledge and Kegan Paul, 1951), pp. 165-66.

ing in the mass media, and especially in politics and religion, is effective in swaying people's thinking and determining their actions.

Ethical Criteria of Communication. Among the basic criteria of ethical judgments in communication are: love, the sacredness of personhood, and the Golden Rule or reciprocity. There are others, of course, but they all are oriented to love, and serve to provide structure, direction, and concreteness to love.

Love is the most ambiguous term in the English language. But, as we discussed in chapter two, the biblical term for love is *agape* and means to will the well-being of the other. Love in this sense is the central ethical motif of the Judeo-Christian tradition and takes a variety of forms in the major religions of the world. There is no English equivalent for agape, but care, compassion, and concern are related words.

Those in the healing profession must sincerely care for patients, because patients can easily sense whether or not the physician or therapist has authentic concern.

At the request of the resident psychiatrist, I interviewed a patient on the ward who insisted that she could not get out of her wheelchair without help. Neither could she care for herself in the most elementary functions. I identified myself as the theological consultant of the psychiatric clinic and urged her to get up and walk. Her response, "You really don't care for me! You only came to see me because you get paid for it!"

Somewhat defensively, I continued to function in my role as "chaplain"; so in a brief prayer, I asked God to give her the will to get up and walk. She compulsively interrupted, exclaiming she never wanted to see me again. She was obviously angry, struggled up out of her wheelchair, walked out of her room (verbally berating me as she left), and joined other patients in the lounge. At first, I was resentful at her outburst. But as I reflected on this within the protective walls of my office, I realized that the anger she had verbalized had also been a strengthening force enabling her to accomplish what she insisted she could *not* do, that is, leave her wheelchair. This encounter appeared to provide a catalyst for her improvement. After this incident, it was easier to convince her of my genuine care for her as a person especially when she learned that I was *not* being paid at that time by the clinic to see her.

Another ethical principle in communication is that of the sacredness of humanhood. In the Judeo-Christian tradition, man is made in the *imago Dei*. As such this gives him dignity and worth as a human being. He is not an It but a Thou, a person and not a thing. Physicians and therapists are bound by their ethical codes to see individuals as persons and not mere cases. The minimum morality in relation to patients is *primum, non nocere* (first, to do no harm). To put it positively, the physician's primary aim is the well-being of the patient as a person.

Imagination is important in the practice of the Golden Principle. It requires empathy, putting oneself in the place and person of the other. John Howard Griffin, author of the powerful book, *Black Like Me*, ingested medication to turn his skin dark in order to live sensitively with Blacks and approximate their struggles. In relating to patients, it is essential that we make the imaginative leap and seek sensitively to understand their fears, hopes, and needs.

Communicating with Terminally Ill Patients

One of the most difficult problems a physician faces is that of what to tell a terminally ill patient. What should the patient be told, when, and how? The significance of these questions in the physician-patient relationship is pointed up by Dr. Donald Oken, Assistant Director, Institute for Psychosomatic and Psychiatric Research and Training in Chicago. He observes: "The manner in which such questions are handled is crucial for the patient and may determine his emotional status and capacity to function from that time on."[4] Under the direction of Oken, a survey was made in 1961 of the policies of 219 physicians about "telling" terminal cancer patients. Ninety percent indicated a preference for not telling the patient that he or she has terminal cancer. Indeed, the majority rarely volunteered this information and none reported a policy of telling every patient. These findings are similar to comparable studies.[5]

As to what the patient should be told, Oken found that there was no uniform policy. Generally the doctor spoke in euphemisms to avoid shocking or traumatizing the patient. Patients were often told simply that they had a "tumor," "lesion," "neoplastic" or "hyperplastic tissue," or suspicious tumor that possibly was benign. If the patient was hesitant

---

[4]Donald Oken, "What to Tell Cancer Patients," *The Journal of the American Medical Association* 175:13 (1 April 1961): 1120-28.

[5]Ibid.

about consenting to surgery or radiation therapy, he was sometimes told that his problem was "pre-cancerous" and that he was lucky that it was discovered early. In Oken's study almost all doctors resorted to such falsification on some occasions. Generally the policy was to tell as little as possible in the most general terms.[6]

As noted above, Oken's questionnaire, administered in 1961, revealed that ninety percent of the physicians responding indicated a preference for not telling a terminal cancer patient his or her diagnosis. To assess attitudinal changes, the same questionnaire was submitted to 699 university hospital medical staff in 1977. Of the 264 respondents, representing a cross section of specialties within the hospital's physician population, ninety percent indicated a preference for telling a terminally ill patient the truth about his or her diagnosis. This is almost a complete reversal of attitude.[7]

Among the basic reasons for the radical attitudinal changes of physicians toward telling the true diagnosis of patients, Dennis Novack, and others, list the following: (1) clinical experience, (2) hospital training, (3) illness in friends or family, and (4) medical school training. Clinical experience was given the major credit. One hundred percent of the respondents stated that patients have a right to know.[8]

Some social and technical factors should also be noted in the changing attitudes of physicians toward truth telling about diagnosis. Among these are: (1) the threat of malpractice lawsuit for a lack of informed consent; (2) laws mandating freedom of information; (3) federal legislation affecting payment of doctors' fees through insurance carriers; and (4) the Professional Review Organization and other professional review agencies like the Food and Drug Administration review of informed consent documents.[9]

There should be added to these factors the enormous amount of death and dying literature of the last decade. Also the fact that now it is legally impossible to offer the patient the opportunity to participate in therapeutic research without his or her full knowledge and consent.

[6]Ibid.

[7]Dennis H. Novack, et al., "Changes in Physicians' Attitudes Toward Telling the Cancer Patient," *The Journal of the American Medical Association* 241:9 (2 March 1979): 897-900.

[8]Ibid., p. 898.

[9]Editorial: "Should the Patient Know?," in ibid., p. 928.

The pros and cons of whether to tell or not to tell the patient the truth have been debated for centuries by philosophers and theologians. For some, speaking and doing the truth is seen to be an absolute. Others argue that, under certain circumstances, to deceive may be the right thing to do. Immanuel Kant, the German philosopher, held that one should always tell the truth regardless of the circumstances or consequences.[10]

Plato, the ancient Greek philosopher, is among the philosophers who make exceptions to truth telling in certain situations. A deception, a falsehood, he thought, should be available to physicians as therapy for patients, but lying for laymen is to be prohibited.[11] Alexandre Dumas, the novelist, echoes this viewpoint. He declares, "When God said that lying is a sin, he made an exception for doctors, and he gave them permission to lie as many times a day as they saw patients."[12]

Theologians from Augustine to the present have differed on truth telling. Augustine, the church father, declared that one should never lie. To get around this strict prohibition, Aquinas distinguished three kinds of lies: officious, jocose, and mischievous. The first kind is helpful, the second is told in jest, and the third is malicious. The officious and jocose lies are less sinful. "Mental reservation" was another technique developed by the Catholic moral philosophers to get around Augustine's prohibition of lying. A textbook on medical ethics suggests that doctors and nurses can lie to patients for the patient's well-being. For example, a patient asks if he has a temperature. The medics may reply, "Your temperature is normal today," while making the mental reservation that it is normal for someone in the patient's precise physical condition.[13]

Deception is advocated by some as a therapeutic tool. Dr. Oliver Wendell Holmes advised physicians to deceive the ill and dying for the patient's own best interests.[14] Arguments for "benevolent deception" or nondisclosure run as follows: (1) complete information is impossible about the state of a patient and, therefore, erroneous data is justified; (2) patients really don't want to know the truth about their condition if it is

[10]*Critique of Practical Reason and Other Writings in Moral Philosophy* (Chicago: University of Chicago Press, 1949), pp. 346-50.

[11]*The Republic*, book III, 389b (New York: Charles Scribner's Sons, 1928), p. 93.

[12]*Camille*, as cited by Joseph Fletcher, *Morals and Medicine* (Boston: Beacon Press, 1961), p. 34.

[13]Charles J. McFadden, *Medical Ethics* (Philadelphia: F. A. Davis, 1967), p. 391.

[14]*Medical Essays* (Boston: Houghton-Mifflin and Co., 1891), pp. 370-89.

bad; (3) telling the patient his or her real condition might cause depression, cardiac arrest, or suicide.

Joseph Fletcher, a pioneer writer in America on medical ethics, argues that doctors should tell patients the truth even if they don't ask for it. Moreover, patients who refuse to deal with the truth should be confronted with it.[15] Among the arguments for truth telling are the following: (1) Knowing the truth, the patient can plan realistically about what he wants to do as long as he lives: he can make property settlements, funeral arrangements, and get right with God and man. (2) The patient has a right to know the truth and the doctor owes the patient the truth as he owes him his skill, care, and technical powers. (3) The patient is a *Thou* and not an *It* and truth telling is essential to any I-Thou relationship. (4) Once it becomes known that a physician has lied to a patient, other patients may fear that they have a more serious illness instead of what the doctor told them. Joseph Fletcher provides the example of the prize fighter, J. J. Corbett, who died of cancer. *The New York Times* ran the story with the headline: "Ex-Champion Succumbs Here to Cancer; He Believed He Had Heart Disease." His doctor had lied to him. Other doctors protested the publication of the deception because their own patients with heart diseases feared that they also had cancer.[16] (5) There is no evidence that patients commit suicide in even small numbers when told the truth.[17] (6) So-called therapeutic lying undermines the moral relationship between physician and patient.

Consider the following case.

A fifty-eight year old male, a veteran of World War II, and a conservative minister of a small church in rural Kentucky, had surgery for cancer of the stomach at the Veterans Hospital. Informed by the surgeon that all the cancerous growth had been removed from the stomach, the patient immediately began to make plans for the future. He was looking forward to seeing the U.S.A. in his camper. He was not told that the cancer had metastasized to other parts of his body and that there were nodules in his lungs. The doctor conferred with the

---

[15]*Morals and Medicine* (Boston: Beacon Press, 1960).

[16]Ibid., p. 48.

[17]Oken, "What to Tell Cancer Patients."

minister's son-in-law, a medical student, and suggested that his father-in-law not be told of his impending death in the next few months. The rationale for nondisclosure of the truth was that the patient appeared to be happy and hopeful. If he were told the truth, he would become depressed.

The medical student agreed with the surgeon. In your judgment, was this a wise choice? What were the alternatives? What will happen when the patient discovers that the truth about his condition has been withheld? He has since learned the truth and his confidence in both his physician and his son-in-law, who is also a doctor, has been shaken.

The vast majority of cancer patients as well as noncancer patients want to be told about the presence of cancer. William D. Kelly and Stanley R. Frierson, physicians in the Department of Surgery, University of Minnesota Medical School, made a study of two groups, one hundred patients with and one hundred without cancer. The great majority in both groups wanted to be told about the presence of cancer.[18]

Sissela Bok appears to arrive at a realistic conclusion about telling the truth to patients. In her view, concealment, evasion, and withholding information may at times be necessary; but the burden of proof must be on the one who advocates this deception. A decision to deceive must be viewed as "a very unusual step to be talked over with colleagues and others who participate in the care of the patient. Reasons must be set forth and debated, alternatives weighed carefully. At all times, the correct information must go to someone closely related to the family."[19]

The Conduct of Communication

As we have noted, the manner of the "how" of informing terminally ill patients is essential to their emotional stability and sense of well-being. How can the physician communicate with the patient so as to maximize the patient's trust, hope, and effort to adjust to being a victim of cancer?

One answer to this question was provided by a former cancer patient. She asserted that the key to telling a patient that he or she has cancer is sensitivity. This implies a sympathetic responsiveness to the attitudes,

[18]"Do Cancer Patients Want to Be Told?" *Surgery* 27 (1950): 822-26.

[19]*Lying: Moral Choice in Public and Private Life* (New York: Pantheon Books, 1978), pp. 238-39.

feelings, and circumstances of others. Recently, a female patient in her mid-fifties was told by her physician that she had cancer. She became emotional and began to cry. At this point he doctor declared: "If you are going to be emotional about this, you will have to see a psychiatrist." She was devastated, and, at that moment, the doctor lost his patient in terms of trust, confidence, and respect. If the doctor loses his patient emotionally, it is almost inevitable that he will lose this patient physically. A healthy physician-patient relationship is essential to the healing process.

Along with the sensitivity essential in this relationship is the concomitant sense of timing. This skill of perception, like any fine-tuned ability, is sharpened with practice. According to one skilled physician who has dealt with numerous terminal patients, a refined sense of timing should determine doctor-patient discussion regarding the seriousness of terminal illness.

For example, the physician should guard against specificity until his attunement to the undertones of the patient's questions and/or conversation alerts him that the patient is ready to talk. In other words, the doctor allows the patient to take the initiative. A gentle "Can I be of any help in answering questions you might have?" might allow the patient to begin to verbalize concerns.

If the patient is unresponsive, further probing could cause estrangement and anger, especially if he or she is in the denial stage. For a patient who continues to refuse to face the reality of the terminal illness, a caring statement which might be helpful could be: "People in your condition often have specific concerns. Are there any particular ones you feel I could help you with?" A sensitive physician will not ask this "on the run," but rather communicate via body language and direct eye contact that what is being said verbally is of tremendous importance.

Sometimes a more direct approach is necessary. The physician may need to say to the patient, "I believe we had better face the facts of your illness," then move into a more explicit description of the patient's condition, while concurrently maintaining a professional optimism.

Again, a realistic optimism is therapeutic in physician-patient relations. Superoptimism, however, may not be possible for such as the oncologist. His is a most vexing profession with enormous psychological and physical demands. Often he finds himself on the edge of exhaustion and despair while engaged in a profession where there are few success stories. Yet he must be at least a sad optimist. Pessimistic as well as optimistic attitudes of the doctor are contagious. And, as the plate or film in photography responds to the light of a specified wave length, so the patient resonates with the attitudes of the healing team. Pessimism is a morbid attitude for the healthy; it is toxic for the sick.

Donald Oken discovered in his study (noted above) of the 219 doctors that a large number of them harbored a deep pessimism about cancer and they tended to avoid research and teaching regarding communications with cancer patients. He noted the need for physicians like himself to seek to overcome the spirit of pessimism.[20]

A doctor who has become depressed should seek psychiatric help. Some doctors delay in seeking even physical, and especially psychotherapeutic, help. Recently in Louisville we had several suicides among doctors on the medical staff and in the community. A brilliant young oncologist became deeply depressed over a period of three years. Friends urged him to get psychiatric help because of the tremendous burdens he was carrying. He refused on the grounds that to do so might cause people to question his competency as a physician. Finally, he committed suicide.

Last, but not least, hope is essential in treating terminally ill patients. The physician walks a tightrope in his attempt to provide patients with facts about their condition and at the same time bolster their hope. A problem is that of how much information is compatible with the maintenance of hope. When doctors lose hope, so do their patients. And how can a despairing person deal constructively with deadly disease?

Maintenance of hope in patients should be a team endeavor. Physician, chaplain, family, and hospital staff working together can establish a support system which will inspire hope in the patient. The role of the chaplain can be most significant in aiding the terminally ill to move through what Elizabeth Kubler-Ross calls the stages of dying: denial, anger, bargaining, depression, and acceptance. (Unfortunately these stages have become universalized; but they apply only to anticipatory, not sudden or traumatic grief.) The following case illustrates the "stages" process. A secretary of the hospital staff asked the chaplain: "How do you deal with one who is dying? It is my mother." At that time the mother with cancer of the throat was in the denial stage. Together the daughter and chaplain sought to sustain her in all the stages to that of acceptance in

---

[20]Oken, "What to Tell Cancer Patients," pp. 1121-28.

which she renewed her vows to God and her church. Her priest visited her and helped to prepare for death. She died with dignity as well as hope.

Kubler-Ross has observed that those with religious faith have an easier time dying.[21] They have hope beyond "this worldly hope men set their hearts upon" that "like snow upon the desert's dusty face lighteth a moment and is gone." Such faith makes it possible to say with the ancient apostle: "We rejoice in our sufferings, knowing that suffering produces endurance, and endurance produces character, and character produces hope, and hope does not disappoint us, because God's love has been poured into our hearts through the Holy Spirit which has been given to us" (Romans 5:3-5, RSV).

---

[21]*On Death and Dying* (New York: Macmillan Co., 1969).

CHAPTER 10

The Ethics of Suicide

In the past decade Western culture has witnessed a renewed interest in the practice of suicide. The morbidly fascinating self-immolation of protesting Buddhist monks in Vietnam during the United States intervention stunned many Americans and caused us to wonder what could possibly motivate "them"—those foreigners—to participate in such obviously self-destructive behavior. But clearly this type of "ultimate solution to problems" is not a culturally defined act endemic to a foreign culture. Suicide is burgeoning in the United States.

Some Statistics on Suicide

Once every minute, according to Karl Menninger, writing in 1957, someone in the United States either attempts suicide or successfully completes the act.[1] In 1975, Alfred Freedman, with others, reported that 25,000 suicides occurred in the United States. Perhaps the actual number was twice that reported, and attempts eight times the number of suicides

---

[1]E. S. Shneidman and Norman L Farberow, *Clues to Suicide* (New York: McGraw-Hill, 1957), Foreword.

reported.[2] Almost 5,000 young people commit suicide each year. This is an increase double the rate of ten years ago and three times as many as twenty years ago. Hence, suicide ranks as the second highest cause of death among young people in this nation. (Accidents rank first.) More suicides occur among those fifteen to twenty-four years old than any other population group.[3]

Even among younger children, aged ten to fourteen, suicides increased during the 1968-1976 period. The number of suicide-related emergencies referred to the Bingham Child Guidance Center in Louisville, Kentucky, increased from twenty-three in 1973 to 150 in 1979.[4]

Suicide occurs among all races, classes, religious groups, and professions. According to several studies, physicians as a group have one of the highest suicide rates, which accounts for up to three percent of the total number of deaths in this profession. Psychiatrists, it is reported, have the highest suicide rate among physicians. However, this data is challenged by Charles Rich and Ferris N. Pitts, Jr. whose report on suicide by male physicians during a five year period (22 May 1967 to 30 May 1972) indicated that the suicide rate among the 17,979 did not differ from the suicide rate for white males over twenty-five.[5] At any rate, the data is equivocal and there is a need for more research on the subject.

According to John J. Schwab, Chairman and Professor of Psychiatry, University of Louisville School of Medicine, as well as most of the psychiatric community, depression is the most lethal of all mental disorders. Indeed, most suicide attempts are made by depressed persons. Diagnosis of depression, therefore, is one of the first important steps in the prevention of suicide.[6]

---

[2]Alfred Freedman, Harold Kaplan, and Benjamin Sadock, eds., *Comprehensive Textbook of Psychiatry*, 2nd ed. (Baltimore: Williams and Wilkins Co., 1975), p. 1783.

[3]Department of Health, Education and Welfare. Reported by Victoria Graham, in *The Louisville Times*, 21 July 1978, p. E-1.

[4]*The Louisville Times*, 10 October 1980, Metro Edition, p. B-1.

[5]Charles L. Rich and Ferris N. Pitts, Jr., "Suicide By Male Physicians During a Five Year Period," *American Journal of Psychiatry* 136:8 (August 1979):1089-90; Freedman, et al., *Comprehensive Textbook of Psychiatry*, p. 1777.

[6]*Handbook of Psychiatric Consultation* (New York: Appleton-Century-Crofts, 1978), p. 164.

Types of Suicide

Although each suicide is, in a sense, unique, there are factors involved which can be categorized in general terms. James Hillman describes collective, symbolic, emotional, and intellectual suicides.[7] I shall deal briefly with *irrational, rational, ambiguous,* and *collective* suicide.

Irrational suicide is deliberate self-termination performed by a deeply distressed or profoundly emotionally ill person. The pressures, traumas, and methodology involved in each case vary, but the result is equally final.

For some, this finality is calculatingly sought and mapped out without the usual distraught dynamics of the emotionally ill. This is termed *rational suicide.* A dramatic historical example of this type of planned suicide was that of the carefully detailed mass deaths of the Jews at Masada in 72 A.D. who covenanted as a community to die by their own hand rather than surrender to the Roman conquerors. Atop their almost inaccessible mountain stronghold, these Jewish patriots chose by lottery those who would execute their self-destruction, at the same time leaving foodstuffs and other supplies as a flagrant, unmistakable message to the Romans that this death was of their own design—thus robbing the invaders of satisfaction. More recently, in 1979, Jo Roman, a sixty-two-year-old New York artist who had been diagnosed as a cancer patient, wrote a 250-page book proclaiming her right to die and had videotaped lengthy hours of elated discussion with her family and friends. Then she bade these people farewell, prepared her box of memorabilia—her "life sculpture"—she hoped would be displayed at a gallery someday, donned her favorite pink nightie and took her Seconal pills.[8]

Similarly, Dr. and Mrs. Henry P. Van Dusen sought to orchestrate their departure from this life. Van Dusen, noted theologian, former president of Union Theological Seminary, noted author of numerous books on theology and ecumenism, and Mrs. Van Dusen were both experiencing debilitating old age and illness. They agreed on a suicide pact after long deliberation and open discussion with those close to them. Both had consulted with the Euthanasia Council of New York City and had signed the Living Will. They left the following poignant letter.

To all Friends and Relations,

We hope that you will understand what we have done even

---

[7]James Hillman, *Suicide and the Soul* (New York: Harper and Row, 1964), pp. 38-41.

[8]*Newsweek*, 2 July 1979, p. 87.

though some of you will disapprove of it and some be disillu-
sioned by it.

We have both had very full and satisfying lives. Pitney has
worked hard and with great dedication for the church. I have
had an adventurous and happy life. We have both had happy
lives and our children have crowned this happiness.

But since Pitney had his stroke five years ago, we have not
been able to do any of the things we want to do and were able
to do, and my arthritis is much worse.

There are too many helpless old people who without
modern medical care would have died, and we feel God would
have allowed them to die when their time had come.

Nowadays it is difficult to die. We feel that this way we are
taking will become more usual and acceptable as the years
pass.

Of course the thought of our children and our grandchildren makes us sad, be we still feel that this is the best way and
the right way to go. We are both increasingly weak and unwell
and who would want to die in a nursing home.

We are not afraid to die.

We send you all our love and gratitude for your wonderful
support and friendship.

"O Lamb of God that takest away the sins of the world,
Have mercy upon us.

"O Lamb of God that takest away the sins of the world,
Grant us thy peace."

Sincerely,
(Elizabeth B. Van Dusen)
(Henry P. Van Dusen)[9]

Another category can be designated as the "equivocal," suspicious or
ambiguous suicide. Numerous cases of "questionable"—not proved—
suicides are registered often. For example, highway accidents that have
no mechanical, weather-related, or health-related causative factors could
possibly be the result of impulsive responses of a death-seeking individual. One patient in our hospital had deliberately involved his small

---

[9]"The Van Dusens' Letter," *People* 3:10 (17 March 1975): 40-43.

foreign car in a collision with an eighteen-wheeler truck on the highway. He had hoped to die.

Another general category can be termed *collective suicide*, which involves some measure of both rational and irrational thinking, but in which the latter dominates the former. An example of this can be seen in the mass suicides at Jonestown, Guyana, in 1978. The carefully planned, well-rehearsed mode of self-slaughter evidently was accepted by most participants with a passivity and self-surrender which appears irrational. The cultic aspects of the Peoples Temple members' life together seemingly contributed to the pathology of this tragedy.

Causes of Suicide

The etiology of suicide involves multifactoral causes: psychopathological, sociological, ecological, and physiological. Hence there is no adequate and secure classification in this field.

Sigmund Freud refers to pent-up, aggressive guilt feelings in which aggression is turned inward upon the self. This relates to Freud's hypothesis of a death wish as a compulsion to reverse the evolutionary process and return to the equilibrium of death. However, this view is not widely held today.[10]

The sociological theory espoused by Emile Durkheim is that suicide is caused by social conditions.[11] He feels that suicide results from the lack of integration of the individual into society.

One of the specific factors in suicide is that of depression. It is generally agreed that most suicidal attempts are made by depressed persons. Other criteria in the etiology of suicide include loneliness, isolation, inability to give or receive love, desire to avoid disgrace, desire for revenge, pressure and competition, and a sense of total failure.

Suicidal Ideation: Assessment of Lethality

Recognizing clues to potential suicide attempts merits a measure of awareness of the following criteria:

- family history of suicide
- previous attempts

---

[10]"Mourning and Melancholy," *Collected Papers*, vol. 4 (London, 1925); cf. Karl Menninger, *Man Against Himself.*

[11]*Suicide: A Study in Sociology* (Glencoe, IL: Free Press, 1951).

- feelings of rejection, uselessness, hopelessness, and/or exhaustion
- specific plans for suicide (such as, changing insurance plans, wills, bidding farewell, and so forth)
- loss of a significant other by death, divorce, separation
- loss of job, money, prestige, or status
- threat of prosecution, criminal involvement, or exposure
- strong feelings of guilt, shame, anger, rage, or revenge
- frustrated dependency
- severe chronic, painful illness
- deep, unrelieved depression.

Awareness of the above criteria can also be balanced with a debunking of some widely held myths. Lists of fables and facts are presented by suicidologists.[12] Below are some of them.

Myth: People who talk about suicide never commit it.
Fact: Eight out of ten persons who kill themselves have talked about it.

Myth: Suicide happens without warning.
Fact: Suicidal persons usually provide numerous clues about their intentions to end their lives.

Myth: People who are suicidal really are intent on dying.
Fact: The death wish is ambivalent. Suicidal persons appear to want to live as much as they desire to die.

Myth: Improvement after a suicide attempt means that the individual is no longer a suicide risk.
Fact: Most suicides happen within three months after improvement begins.

Myth: Once suicidal, always suicidal.
Fact: Suicidal persons are only suicidal at delimited periods of time.

Myth: Suicide strikes more often among the wealthy.
Fact: It strikes among all levels of society.

Myth: Suicide is hereditary.
Fact: Studies reveal suicide is an individual act and not necessarily affected by genetically related mental illness.

---

[12]Schneidman and Farberow, *Clues to Suicide*; Freedman, et. al., *Comprehensive Textbook of Psychiatry*, pp. 1783-84.

Myth: All suicidal persons are mentally ill.
Fact: Not necessarily so. The quality of reason and logic is just as prevalent as the quality of anxiety and emotional disturbances.
Myth: Suicide is immoral.
Fact: Not always. It depends on time and place. Under certain circumstances some societies accept it as an honorable act.

Management of High Risk Suicide Patients

Having traced some of the trends in history as well as causative factors regarding suicide, we should now turn our attention to dealing positively with the potential suicide victim. Recognition of symptoms and signals is essential. The following chart presents some insights on the demographics of suicide risk.[13]

Demography of Suicide Risk

Factor	Greater Risk
Age	Older than 55 years vs younger
Sex	Male vs female
Race	White vs nonwhite
Geography	Urban vs rural
Marital status	Never married vs divorced vs married vs married with children
Employment	Unemployed vs employed
Medical status	Chronic or terminal illness; intractable pain
Suicide history	Previous attempt vs first attempt

Since attempted suicide is usually maladaptive behavior embedded in psychiatric illness syndromes, the intervention of psychiatrically-trained personnel is optimal. Where lethality is high, hospitalization is essential. But even the paramedical or nonprofessional can cooperate in the following ways:

- Maintain contact with the person.
- Seek to help improve his/her self-image.
- Seek to involve him/her in activity.
- Try to build a strong support system.

---

[13]"Caring For the Suicidal Patient" in *Patient Care* 14:20 (30 November 1980): 109.

- Seek to engage in a logotherapeutic "finding-a-reason-to-live" exercise.
- Explore with the patient reasons to "hope."

Above all, if possible, instill and kindle a flame of hope. For where there is hope there is life. A deeply depressed female college student was asked by her psychiatrist if she ever thought of suicide. Her response was in the affirmative. "Yes," she replied, "but then I fear that if I do, something wonderful may be just around the corner and I would miss it."

In addition to hospitals, police agencies, and emergency medical services, community resources may include a "hot-line" in a suicide crisis center. Those manning these lines can ultilize preventive techniques which include trying to: (1) convince the caller that you want to help him and maintain contact; (2) focus on the lethality of the crisis: (a) the stress the person is currently suffering; (b) the tone of voice as well as what he/she says; (c) his/her suicide plan—how? when? where?; (d) the person's character structure; (e) his/her physical and psychological symptoms, that is, complaints; and (f) what resources the person has— friends? relatives? money? (isolation increases lethality).

In such cases, one would try to persuade the suicidal person to go voluntarily to a hospital or helping agency. Another alternative (for example, for a family trying to prevent a family member from attempting suicide) would be following the Mental Inquest Warrant (MIW) or Involuntary Emergency Detention procedure. Check the laws of your state and the procedures of committing a suicidal person for hospitalization.

Postvention care of the survivors of the person who has terminated his or her life is very important. Helpful counsel on the part of the family doctor may be a significant resource. Psychotherapy may be in order and should be started for the survivors as soon as possible, especially where children are involved.

The Ethics of Suicide

Having dealt with some of the strategies for prevention of suicide let us now turn to the ethical dimensions of the problem. Arguments pro and con concerning the morality of self-detruction range all across the ethical spectrum.

Plato generally condemned it, but he made an exception in the case of intolerable stress or major disgrace. He maintained, however, that those who chose death in this manner must be buried separately from those who died by natural death.[14]

Aristotle viewed suicide unequivocally as an act of cowardice and an act of offense against the state.[15] On the other hand, the Stoics claimed that suicide was a reasonable exercise of human freedom. However, this view was not a dominant one among minority schools of Greek philosophers. The Stoics justified suicide for reasons of long and painful illness, madness, and immoral behavior.

The biblical record contains a number of references to individuals who chose suicide: Abimelech, to save himself from the disgrace of being killed by a woman (Judges 9:54); Samson, who destroyed the Philistines with himself (Judges 16:30); Saul, who fell upon his own sword (1 Samuel 31:4); Ahithophel, who hanged himself because his counsel was rejected (2 Samuel 17:23); Zimri, who burned himself in his house (1 Kings 16:18); Razis, who chose suicide rather than to fall into the hands of the enemies (2 Maccabees 14:41); Judas, who hanged himself (Matthew 27:5); and the Philippian jailer, who attempted suicide, fearing the prisoners had escaped (Acts 16:27).

Some of the above who committed suicide were extolled for their valor in choosing suicide (Saul and Razis) while the suicides of Abimelech, Samson, and Ahithophel were described in neutral terms. On the other hand, the suicides of Zimri and Judas were interpreted by biblical writers as punishments for their sins. The jailer's act was due to terror. This variance of stance was altered after the Babylonian Exile, and the later Jewish writers condemned the termination of one's own life. At any rate, the Jewish emphasis on the value of human life would render suicide anomalous.

The Early Church Fathers wrestled with this problem, too. Augustine formulated a Christian doctrine of suicide in *The City of God*.[16] He condemned suicide on three grounds: (1) it violates the commandment: "Thou shalt not kill"; (2) it precludes an opportunity for repentance; and (3) it is a cowardly act.

Aquinas elaborated on the church doctrine regarding suicide. He opposed it because (1) suicide is in opposition to nature and to proper

---

[14]*Laws*, book I, x.

[15]*Nichomachean Ethics*, V:11; cf. III:8.

[16]Augustine, *The City of God*, book I, chapters 4-26.

self-life; (2) God alone has control over life and death; (3) to decide one's own death usurps God's power; (4) it is an offense against the community; and (5) contrary to the widely held view of his day that a virgin should kill herself if she were forced to lose her chastity, Aquinas held (as did Augustine) that virtue was of the mind and will and thus is not lost if compelled by force, so suicide was unnecessary in such cases. Aquinas held that the suicide of Samson was under divine inspiration.[17]

The Augustinian-Thomist view is the basis for the current orthodox Catholic view of suicide. This view holds: (1) that suicide is a violation of the commandment, "Thou shalt not kill"; (2) that it is contrary to nature; (3) that it is usurpation of God's prerogative; (4) that it is a social wrong; (5) that it excludes repentance; and (6) that natural death provides opportunity to demonstrate courage. But there are two exceptions: suicide by divine inspiration, such as that of Samson and some saints of the church; and the method used by the state to execute those guilty of capital crimes.

Through the centuries, however, there have been challenges to the church's posture on suicide. Some Christians have sought to justify suicide. John Donne, for example, in his *Biathanatos* (1644) attempted to prove that suicide under certain conditions was not incompatible with reason or God.

More recently, there are indications that suicide is becoming more acceptable as a means of terminating one's life under certain circumstances. It is reported that Bishop Francis Simon of Indore, India, has supported suicide in cases where an individual might be likely to divulge nationally sensitive, classified, or secret information under torture.[18] The United States intelligence agencies, as well as those of other countries, often provide suicide capsules to strategic agents, such as U-2 pilot Francis Gary Powers who declined to use his when captured by the Russians.

During the last two decades ethicists have been challenged by suicide in the context of new medical technologies which make it possible to keep a patient alive even though he is enduring an unacceptable quality of life. The moral theologians are divided in their responses to this problem. Paul Ramsey, Professor of Christian Ethics at Princeton University,

---

[17]*Summa Theologica*, II, III, 8:64, article 5.

[18]John Deedy, "The Morality of Self-Destruction," *The New York Times*, 2 March 1975.

argues that life is a gift and to choose death is to throw the gift back to the giver. He concludes that we are stewards of life, not owners, to do what we will with it.[19]

On the other hand, Daniel C. Maguire, an ex-priest, formerly of the Catholic University of America and now professor at Marquette University, a Jesuit institution, rejects the idea that every form of self-killing is murder. Rather he thinks that to bring death by suicide, when death is the only remaining relief, may be a positive moral action.[20] Likewise, Dr. John C. Bennett, noted Protestant theologian and ethicist, asserts that suicide may be morally justified under certain circumstances such as terminal illness and an unacceptable quality of life.[21]

There is no adequate theology of suicide; the church generally stands opposed to self-killing. But there is a growing acceptance of passive euthanasia as indicated in the current literature and by the distribution of hundreds of thousands of copies of the Living Will by the Euthanasia Society of America. And it appears that in our present-day society church members are less likely to condemn those who choose to terminate their own lives.

Another indication that the moral condemnation of suicide is lessening is the response of thousands of people to a "do it yourself" manual on suicide, published by Exit, a British organization dedicated to the right to die with dignity. The book, *A Guide to Self-Deliverance*, provides information on how to "bloodlessly and non-violently" terminate the life of incurably ill, aged, and incapacitated persons.[22] One of the dangers inherent in the distribution of this booklet is the possibility that it might fall into the hands of depressed individuals and discourage them from seeking psychiatric help.

Physicians have an ethical responsibility to be sensitive to the dynamics of the suicidal patient and in diagnosing such symptoms. Prescription of drugs should be carefully monitored to avoid placing in the hands of the suicidal person a means of ending his life. Overprescribing drugs to which the patient may become addicted or which may cause depression

---

[19]*Ethics at the Edges of Life: Medical and Legal Intersections* (New Haven: Yale University Press, 1978), p. 146.

[20]Deedy, "The Morality of Self-Destruction."

[21]Ibid.

[22]"A Manual On How To Commit Suicide," *Newsweek*, 7 April 1980, p. 77.

should be recognized as a possible hazard. Such patients should not be released prematurely.

It is the ethical responsibility of the physician to aid in building a strong support system for suicidal patients when they leave the hospital. It is not enough just to provide medication and psychotherapy. Helping to enlist a congenial person or group to give the patient support and inner strength is a part of the total healing process.

In conclusion, consider the following suggestions. Suicide is a serious moral issue requiring more creative means of prevention and care. Research into the dynamics and diagnosis should be intensified and subsidized by insurance companies which have a financial interest in reducing the mortality rate by suicide. To assert, as does Thomas Szasz, M.D., that suicide is a "basic human right," regardless of the circumces, is an absolutist position which does not take into account the situation.[23] When a person becomes incurably ill, unproductive, and a victim of an intolerable quality of life, and death is the one means of relief, the individual may be morally justified to choose to self-destruct. For love wills the well-being of the other and the self is also an other.

---

[23]*The Theology of Medicine* (New York: Harper and Row, 1977), p. 32 and chapter 6: "The Ethics of Suicide."

Chapter 11

Death: Elective and Esthetic

Each year two million people die in the United States. Worldwide, hundreds of millions die. Death may be prolonged, but it is inevitable. Sooner or later the rider of the pale horse of the apocalypse will overtake each one of us. Benjamin Franklin observed: "In this world nothing is certain but death and taxes." Shakespeare has one of his characters put it graphically: "By medicine my life may be prolonged, yet death will seize the doctor, too."

Man is the only animal that knows he is going to die and that death is inevitable for everyone. He has, in recent years, developed technologies to prolong life and this has resulted in a cluster of critical ethical questions. Does a patient with a terminal disease have a right to choose the time and the manner of death? Does such a person have the right to reject mechanical means such as the respirator which may prolong life a few more painful weeks or months? Does the patient have a right to elective death? Does biological life supersede meaningful life? In short, does a person with a terminal disease or injury have the right to die by decision and with dignity?

In the last two decades, our nation has witnessed a growing movement on behalf of the right of the individual to die in dignity. When life is no longer meaningful, it is argued, one should have the right to terminate life. Quality of life takes precedence over quantity of life. In spite of the fact that Americans tend to avoid thinking about death, the subject has become academically popular. Thanatologists are sought after for lectures; thousands of volumes pour from the presses on death and dying; articles in learned journals, in magazines, and newspapers attract millions of readers; seminars on death have become so popular that some lecturers travel the circuit full-time talking about death. Death is a popular subject for dramatic and literary productions. The Euthanasia Educational Society is alive and well and distributing a record amount of literature.

Toward a Definition of Death

When is an individual dead? There is no simple answer to this question, for death is a complex phenomenon. Physicians who deal with the death of patients desire some definition to protect them legally. Lawsuits are becoming common especially in relating to medical procedures like euthanasia and organ transplants. Lawyers need some definition of death for those cases involving ambiguity and uncertainty about death and those responsible for it.

Death is a process and this fact makes it difficult to define it. There is the social dimension or interpersonal relationships which usually die first.[1] Physical death has several stages: (1) *clinical death* in which breathing and heartbeat stop; (2) *brain death,* which follows immediately—the higher brain first and then the lower one; (3) *biological death,* which occurs due to the cessation of heartbeat and respiratory functions; and, finally, (4) *cellular death* in which some parts of the body die more rapidly than others due to different cell composition.[2]

Biological death, the traditional criterion of death, no longer applies in the light of biomedical technologies to sustain biological life. Both physician and lawyer need a more precise view of death. The "Report of the Ad Hoc Committee of the Harvard School of Medicine to Examine

---

[1]T. W. Furlow, "Tyranny of Technology, A Physician Looks at Euthanasia," *The Humanist* 34:4 (1974): 6-8.

[2]James B. Nelson, *Human Medicine* (Minneapolis: Augsburg Publishing House, 1973), p. 126.

the Definition of Brain Death" makes a significant contribution to this end. The content of this report makes it less difficult to ascertain death. (See Appendix C.) Basically, the committee defined death as the irreversible coma which results in the cessation of both higher and lower brain functioning and consequently the permanent loss of heart and respiratory function. Careful procedures are established for making certain that death as described has taken place.

Since the Harvard report, several states have enacted legislation attempting to define death. Kansas was the first to do so. That legal definition makes either the absence of heart and respiratory function or the absence of spontaneous brain function the medical and legal indication of death.[3]

But death is not only social and physical; it is also an "emotional-spiritual" process. Elizabeth Kubler-Ross, psychiatrist, in her popular book, *On Death and Dying*, describes the emotional stages of those who have learned that they are terminally ill. Kubler-Ross identifies five stages between awareness of seriousness and death. These are: (1) *denial* of any serious illness, but most patients cease denial sooner or later; (2) *anger* after the truth breaks through: the patient asks, "Why me?," and he or she becomes difficult, critical of others, and demanding; (3) the *bargaining* stage in which the patient may pray for an extension of life, in exchange for which they promise to be good, go to church, and do good works; (4) the *depression* stage in which the patient fully realizes the fact of terminal illness and becomes very depressed; and (5) *acceptance*, the stage at which the patient declares, "I am ready to go and all is well."[4]

This entire schemata of Kubler-Ross has tended to become a blueprint for many medical team members who assiduously monitor terminal patients for evidences of each identifiable stage. However, dying patients cannot be stereotyped and forced in toto into a given developmental system: patients are indeed unique entities, and these stages are merely general categories. For example, some patients belie the category of acceptance by refusing to accept the reality of impending death.

Euthanasia: Pro and Con

Euthanasia is the traditional term for dying with dignity. It is derived from the Greek *eu*, good, and *thanatos*, death. In current discussions

---

[3]I. M. Kennedy, "The Kansas Statute on Death—An Appraisal," *The New England Journal of Medicine* 285:17 (21 October 1970): 496.

[4]*On Death and Dying* (New York: Macmillan Co., 1969), chs. 3-7.

euthanasia is variously referred to as "mercy killing," "elective death," "allowing one to die," "death with dignity," or even as murder.

Euthanasia may be direct or indirect (also referred to as active and passive, positive and negative euthanasia). *Direct* or *active* euthanasia is a *deliberate action* to shorten or to end the life of the terminally ill person. For example, a person afflicted with a terminal illness, and who wants to die, may receive an injection of air into the blood or circulatory system to cause a fatal embolism. Under our present laws, this action would legally be judged as a murder. *Indirect* or *negative* euthanasia may be accomplished by *stopping treatments* that prolong the patient's life, such as by "pulling the plug" that keeps the respirator working; or by *withholding treatment* altogether, such as when a badly malformed baby is not respirated at birth.

Arguments are presented for and against active or direct euthanasia. Some of the points debated pro and con are as follows:

Con: Euthanasia is murder.

Pro: But murder is unlawful killing of a human being with *malice* aforethought.

Con: Euthanasia violates the injunction, "Thou shalt not kill."

Pro: But the commandment means "no murder." Those who justify war and capital punishment cannot condemn euthanasia on this ground.

Con: God must decide who shall live and who shall die.

Pro: If this is a valid argument, then it is also wrong to seek to prolong life.

Con: Suffering is a part of the divine plan and the terminally ill person should live through the pain until the end.

Pro: The Bible teaches us to be "merciful," and ending the life of an incurably suffering patient is an act of mercy.

Con: The sanctity of life forbids euthanasia.

Pro: The notion that life is absolutely sacred is not Christian. Some things are more valuable than life itself. Christian martyrs knew this. Life is not the highest good; the quality of life is more important than mere physical existence.

Con: One should do everything to save a life no matter the cost.

Pro: It is not right to bankrupt a family with hospital and medical costs when there is no hope for the recovery of the patient.

My own position is that neither indirect nor direct euthanasia should be absolutized. However, I feel more comfortable with the indirect method. The patient's wish that treatment be withdrawn should be honored. It is true that the conscious patient may make the decision impulsively or under extreme pain. But a safeguard can be established by requiring a time lag between the patient's decision and the withdrawal of treatment in order to accommodate a change of mind. If the patient is unconscious or in a coma, the decision could be made by the family in consultation with a team of doctors, nurses, and a clergyman.

Indirect euthanasia for the terminally ill person is morally defensible because it is in harmony with the Christian ethic of love. It allows the patient to die with a measure of dignity. Also this may save the family from bankruptcy due to the enormous cost involved in keeping the patient alive, enduring a quality of life which essentially is intolerable.

Some Ethical Reflections

Christian moral thinkers differ on the issue of euthanasia. Roman Catholic ethicists oppose any action which has as its primary intention the direct killing of a terminally ill patient. This holds even if such measures are requested by the patient. However, this rule is modified or qualified by the principle of "double-effect." According to this principle, two effects might result in an action: one good and *intended* and the other one evil and *unintended.* For example, a patient may be given a pain-easing drug that is lethal and the patient dies. The *intent* was to ease the pain of the patient; but the consequence of the action involved certain but *unintended* death.

Protestant moral thinkers differ among themselves about the issue of euthanasia. Theologians Karl Barth and Dietrich Bonhoeffer held that direct action of any sort to kill a patient is playing God and usurping His right to define the limits of life, an action which, morally speaking, is murder. For them, both voluntary and compulsory termination of human life by direct means are rejected.

Barth declared that "it is for God and God alone to make an end of human life, and that man should help in this only when he has a specific and clear command from God."[5] The latter part of this statement seemed to imply that there is allowance for the "exceptional case." A few pages

---

[5]*Church Dogmatics* III/4, (Edinburgh: T. and T. Clark, 1961), p. 422.

on, Barth seemed to support this exception.[6] At best, his position is paradoxical.

Bonhoeffer stated that God alone is the author and the finisher of life and in the sight of God there is no life that is not worth living.[7] But he failed to apply these principles—at least once—to his own life for he joined a group plotting to assassinate Hitler.

Paul Ramsey, Professor of Christian Ethics at Princeton University, rejects direct killing of the patient *in extremis*, but he appears to be open to indirect euthanasia. He would agree that it is morally defensible under the rule of double effect to use pain-relieving drugs which may also result in shortening the patient's life. But he rejects direct killing. Withholding treatment, he thinks, is different from directly killing, and is morally acceptable. Because the patient, he observes, "dies his own death from causes that it is no longer merciful or reasonable to fight by means of possible medical interventions."[8]

Joseph Fletcher, Professor of Medical Ethics at the University of Virginia, believes that both indirect and direct euthanasia are the same in principle. He asks: "What, morally, is the difference between doing nothing to keep the patient alive and giving a fatal dose of pain-killing or lethal drug? The intention is the same, either way. A decision *not* to keep the patient alive is as morally deliberate as a decision to *end* a life."[9]

What shall we make of all these views on euthanasia? To say, as Barth does, that God alone is to end life is questionable theology. If God alone ends life, we must refrain from medical intervention of any disease at any stage of the illness. The "double effect" approach of Ramsey and others has problems. The giving of a pain-relieving drug with the *intent* to relieve pain knowing that it will end the patient's life is difficult to distinguish from direct killing. The intent is the same and so is the consequence. It is also, as Harmon Smith notes, "too subtle and fine to be of much practical help in decision making."[10] As for Fletcher's view, he makes a too easy identification of direct and indirect killing of the patient. Granted that the intention and the consequences appear to be the same,

[6]Ibid., p. 427.

[7]*Ethics* (London: SCM Press, 1955), p. 119.

[8]*The Patient as a Person* (New Haven: Yale University Press, 1970), p. 151.

[9]*Moral Responsibility* (Philadelphia: Westminster Press, 1967), p. 150.

[10]*Ethics and the New Medicine* (Nashville: Abingdon Press, 1970), p. 31.

the means have moral significance. There may be less guilt about allowing the patient to die than killing him or her.

As for church pronouncements on euthanasia, I can find none in favor of direct killing. Some have endorsed indirect euthansia. The Council for Christian Social Action of the United Church of Christ adopted a statement on the issue in 1973. It reads: "We believe it is ethically and theologically proper for a person to wish to avoid artificial and/or painful prolongation of a terminal illness and for him or her to execute a living will or similar document of instruction." But the Church Council was unable to reach any conclusion about direction to end the life of the terminally ill.

Orthodox Judaism prohibits direct euthanasia but has a permissive attitude toward passive euthanasia. Some Christian moralists, both Protestant and Catholic, declare that the use of extraordinary means to prolong the life of the terminally ill patient is not required.[11]

New Conceptual Models of Decent Death

Some writers are now beginning to reject the use of the term euthanasia for the good death. Arthur Dych, Harvard Divinity School professor, claims that the distinction between indirect and direct euthanasia is too decisive and that these terms should not be used. He prefers the term "benemortasia" meaning a good death in which the patient *in extremis* is allowed or permitted to die.[12] Obviously, this position is closely related to indirect euthanasia.

Paul Ramsey no longer uses the term euthanasia because he thinks it has acquired a meaning similar to that of mercy killing. Because of this identification, Ramsey used the term "agathanasia" to indicate the good death. Agathanasia turns out to be indirect euthanasia with a positive emphasis. The decision not to utilize or to cease to employ life-sustaining technologies is a decision to care realistically for the terminally ill patient and to minister to him or her.[13]

"Antidysthanasia" (against bad death) is the term used by Joseph Fletcher. The term denotes the indirect form of the good death, the

---

[11]George Kieffer, *Bioethics: A Textbook of Issues* (Reading, MA: Addison-Wesley Publishing Co., 1979), p. 221.

[12]William E. May, "Euthanasia, Benemortasia, and the Dying," in Paul Jersild and Dale Johnson, *Moral Issues and Christian Response* (New York: Holt, Rinehart, and Winston, 1971), pp. 399-408.

[13]*The Patient as a Person* (New Haven: Yale University Press, 1970), pp. 149-64.

refusal to prolong a painful state. This can take one of several forms: (1) giving an increased dosage of a pain-killing drug with the intention of relieving pain until a lethal level of toxicity is reached; (2) stopping treatment altogether, such as disconnecting a kidney machine; and (3) withholding treatment altogether, such as refusing to respirate a defective baby at birth.

My own position on terminally ill dying is identified with "kalosthanasia," a neologism. *Kalos* is the Greek for "morally good" and esthetically acceptable. *Thanasia* is from the Greek and means death. The term thus identifies a death that is morally right, dignified, and does not shock one's esthetic sense. It does not absolutize either the passive or active method of dying, but has an openness to the circumstances of the patient. Either may be morally defensible, depending on the situation.

The following is a scenario of active kalosthanasia. The terminally ill patient's cancer has so metastasized that there is no hope of recovery. The patient may linger on a few weeks with a quality of life that is unacceptable. Treatment is useless and the patient is in great pain. The patient at his or her own request could be given increasing doses of a pain-killing drug which would ease the pain and at the same time build up a toxicity that would be lethal. Or the respirator could be adjusted so that the patient would be reduced to only six or seven breaths per minute. Or the patient could receive a lethal injection and die in sleep. This action, of course, would be illegal but not necessarily immoral.

Take the following case of unesthetic death. A man seventy-two years old was in a nursing home. A stroke had left him paralyzed in his left side and arm. Twenty-five percent of his body suffered first degree burns in a recent fire. While I was present with him in his hospital room, he had another of several cardiac arrests. The emergency code alerted the doctor, resuscitation equipment was rushed to the bedside, and massive, urgent efforts were utilized to save this patient's life. Observing this, I had the feeling that the whole scene bordered on the pornographic. Here was a person being restored to an unbearable quality of life. In the end, it would probably bankrupt the family.

My own father became seriously ill in his early seventies. When hospitalized, the diagnosis indicated that a cancer of the stomach had metastasized to other parts of the body. He insisted on the truth about his health and was told that he had only a few weeks or months at most to live. Immediately he insisted on leaving the hospital and he went home to die. His children, grandchildren, great-grandchildren, kin, and friends came by to see him. In spite of the pain and suffering, he kept a good spirit and a sense of humor.

All extraordinary treatment was withdrawn. Only drugs to ease the pain were ingested. His was a kalosthanasia death, both morally right and esthetically acceptable.

Efforts to keep the patient alive are noble as long as there is reasonable hope of recovering with a bearable quality of life. And the patient should be encouraged to strive to recover. As the poet, Dylan Thomas, said of his dying father:

> Do not go gentle into that good night,
> Old age should burn and rave at close of day;
> Rage, rage against the dying light.

But the patient may reach the stage when it becomes realistic to accept the fact of approaching death. Then there may be time to set his house in order, for he is aware that he will die, not live. Rage must cease so that the pilgrim may enter in peace that country from "whose bourn no traveler returns."

To help ensure that no "heroic" medical intervention or "extraordinary means" will be used to keep a terminally ill patient alive, he or she may sign a Living Will. (See Appendix D.) To make the most effective use of a Living Will the Euthanasia Society suggests that you sign and date it before two witnesses, deposit a copy with your doctor and those who are likely to be near you when you are terminally ill, keep the original nearby, discuss your intentions now with those closest to you, and redate your Living Will every year. The Living Will may not stand up in court. In 1974, a committee of 1,776 doctors in New York State called for legislation to make euthanasia legal so that they and their patients may be protected from possible prosecution.[14]

In 1976, California passed the nation's first right-to-die legislation, called the Natural Death Act. The directive to the doctor applies only to the terminally ill patient whose condition will not be changed by the application of life-sustaining procedures which serve only to artificially and unnecessarily prolong the moment of death. The Natural Death Act has many detailed requirements. When the patient requests that his life

---

[14]"Death by Chance, Death by Choice," *Atlantic Monthly* (January 1974): 62.

not be artificially prolonged in a terminal condition, two physicians must agree on the diagnosis of a terminal condition. There must be a fourteen-day waiting period after the terminal condition has been diagnosed and signed by witnesses before the patient's wish for nonheroic measures is legally binding. Only mechanical means to sustain or restore the patient may be withheld or withdrawn and this only where death is imminent. The directive must be signed by two witnesses unrelated to the patient or the health care facility. Women must stipulate that the directive shall be suspended should they become pregnant. In addition, the patient can revoke the directive which expires after five years.

This Natural Death Act is important because it helps to settle legal issues arising from "living wills" in terms of professional liability and insurance coverage. It protects doctors from malpractice suits against hastening the death of the terminally ill patient in terms of the measures in the bill. The effect of living wills on insurance policies is resolved by declaring that death from carrying out the directive does not constitute suicide.[15]

By 1977 bills were pending in more than forty states for right-to-die legislation. Eight have enacted legislation of some form (Arkansas, California, Florida, Idaho, Nevada, New Mexico, North Carolina, and Virginia). Most European countries do not classify passive euthanasia as homicide. Switzerland's laws allow a doctor to leave poison near the terminally ill patient who can ingest it of his own free will. Uruguay was the first nation to legalize active euthanasia performed at the request of the dying patient.[16]

The issue of passive euthanasia is becoming more acceptable to the general public in this country. But this is not the only issue involved in prolonging life. Rather, along with ethical issues are socioeconomic ones. Costs of research, technological equipment, and health care costs continue to burgeon. Who is going to pick up the tab?

Other countries have devised ways to deal with cost factors. For example, Britain's National Health Service has a policy of denying hemodialysis treatment to patients over sixty-five. Sweden routinely denies expensive organ transplants to people over that same age. Ameri-

---

[15]See Michael Garland, "Politics, Legislation, and Natural Death," *The Hastings Center Report* 6:5 (October 1976): 5-6.

[16]Howard Brill, "Death With Dignity: A Recommendation For Statutory Change," *University of Florida Law Review* 22 (1970): 368-83.

cans need to take a long-range, realistic look at the interrelated socioeconomic dynamics of prolonging life, as well as the ethical issues.

CHAPTER 12

Humor as a Therapeutic Tool
in the Healing Process

Man is the only animal that laughs—and knows that he does. This ability to respond to the humorous must indeed be a gift from man's Creator as compensation for homo sapiens' burden of a sense of self-transcendence and the resultant fears, anxieties, and memories of things past as well as anticipations of the future.

Definition of Humor

The term *humor* defies precise definition because of its highly subjective aspects. *Webster's New Collegiate Dictionary* cites its derivation from the Latin *humor*, meaning "moisture," and defines it as: "1 a : a normal functioning bodily semifluid or fluid (as the blood or lymph) b : a secretion (as a hormone) that is an excitant of activity 2 a *in medieval physiology* : a fluid or juice of an animal or plant; *specif* : one of the four fluids [blood, phlegm, choler or yellow bile, and melancholy or black bile] entering into the constitution of the body and determining by their relative proportions a person's health and temperament." Hence, "humor" designates one's disposition, state of mind, or mood. (Humor is actually designated by some as a "social lubricant.")

Some of the characteristics of humor include spontaneity and surprise. The punch line, the pun, the double entendre, the unexpected joviality elicit a kind of recognition of a variant from the usual. Satisfaction in mastering this significance is both reassuring and threat-reducing. Indeed, humor can be a valuable diagnostic tool. But before examining that use, let us first view briefly the history of man's involvement with humor.

Humor and Health in Historical Perspective

The healing power of humor has been known for centuries. Biblical literature contains numerous passages indicating the health-giving nature of humor. Most notable is Proverbs 17:22: "A cheerful heart is a good medicine, but a downcast spirit dries up the bones" (RSV). A closely related idea appears in Proverbs 15:13: "A glad heart makes a cheerful countenance, but by sorrow of heart the spirit is broken" (RSV).

Jesus had a subtle sense of humor.[1] He portrays a hypercritical person as one who has a plank in his own eye and attempts to remove a sawdust grain from another's eye (Matthew 7:1-5). And he describes the legalistic religious leaders of his day as individuals who strain a gnat out of their wine through a cloth, but swallow a camel, hump, hoofs, and all. Both of these animals were considered unclean and, in their efforts to avoid a *tiny* defilement, the Pharisees are polluted by a *huge* defilement (Matthew 23:24).

Throughout the whole of the gospels and epistles there is a note of joy. The gospel itself means "good news" of joy (compare Luke 2:10).

The idea that humor has a healing power is expressed by numerous thinkers. Robert Burton (1577-1640) who wrote *The Anatomy of Melancholy*, one of the first books on depression, could cite a large number of authorities in support of laughter as a healing measure.[2] Immanuel Kant (1724-1804), the German philosopher, held that hearty laughter has a healthful effect on the body and possibly prevents constipation.[3] Sigmund Freud, father of modern psychiatry, wrote a long essay on wit and its relation to the unconscious. He believed that mirth was a "safety

---

[1]Elton Trueblood, *The Humor of Christ* (New York: Harper and Row, 1964).

[2]*The Anatomy of Melancholy* (London: Longman, Rees, Orme and Co., 1827).

[3]Trans. by J. H. Bernard, *Kant's Critique of Judgement*, 2nd ed., revised (London: Macmillan and Co., 1914), pp. 222-26.

valve" for nervous tension. Humor, he held, could be used as an effective therapy in psychoanalysis.[4]

Currently two persons have brought to the public's attention the healing power of humor: Raymond Moody, M.D., and Norman Cousins, formerly editor of the prestigious journal, *The Saturday Review* and now senior lecturer at the School of Medicine, University of California. Moody's book is a scholarly but highly readable work which deals with laughter and humor as they relate to health and pathology. As a practicing physician he uses humor as a therapeutic tool.[5] Cousins wrote a fascinating account of his remarkable recovery from a supposedly terminal disease. His restoration to health, he thinks, was due to the use of his own will to get well and the will to live, and to a physician as a partner who permitted him to follow his own regimen. In addition, he believes that positive thoughts and laughter figured prominently in his recovery. In order to stimulate laughter Cousins arranged to view old films including "Candid Camera" and the Marx Brothers comedies.[6]

Types of Humor

Categorizing humor is also an imprecise exercise. We can, however, point to a few types of humor and subsequent uses.

Genial humor involves a gentle, positive stance toward life in general. This type of humor is characterized by a chuckle, a twinkling eye, a warming smile. It is inclusive and redemptive, causing the other person or persons to feel a glow of acceptance and sharing.

The opposite type of humor is a *destructive* type which is abusive and demeaning. Moody distinguishes between *laughing with* (genially) and *laughing at* (destructively) someone. "In cruel laughter, in laughing at someone we exclude him from the network of love, understanding and support; in laughing with someone we fold him within it."[7]

The sarcastic denigration of another is a double-edged sword which

---

[4]*Jokes and Their Relation to the Unconscious*, trans. by James Strachey (New York: W. W. Norton and Co., 1960); and "Wit and its Relation to the Unconscious" in *The Basic Writings of Sigmund Freud*, trans. and ed. by A. A. Brill (New York: Modern Library, 1938), pp. 633-803; "Humour," *International Journal of Psychoanalysis* 11:1 (1928).

[5]*Laugh After Laugh: The Healing Power of Humor* (Jacksonville, FL: Headwaters Press, 1978).

[6]*Anatomy of an Illness* (New York: W. W. Norton and Co., 1979).

[7]Moody, *Laugh After Laugh*, p. 109.

deepens wounds for the wielder as well as the one who is attacked. Dr. John R. Claypool relates the following incident:

> I was in college, and it so happened that there was another boy in my class who was rather effeminate and spoke in an unusually high, thin voice. One night in a coffee shop his name was mentioned, and I proceeded, to the delight of everyone in my booth, to imitate his voice in a way that was ridicule. At the height of my performance, somebody punched me in the ribs and pointed two booths down; for there, in easy earshot, sitting alone, was none other than the boy himself. I'll never forget his expression of utter humiliation as he dropped his head and rushed out of the building. I felt like the utter heel I was, and nothing else that evening was much fun, for I knew deep down I had purchased a few cheap laughs at the expense of another person's feelings. However, the way I felt that night was not nearly as bad as what I felt the next morning. For you see, it happened to be the day for class elections, and when the floor was opened for nominations for president, lo and behold, the boy with the high, thin voice got up and placed my name in nomination.[8]

Somewhat related to destructive humor is the more subtle *avoidance* type. This is using a joke or superficial laughter as a diversionary tactic to avoid delving into the deeper dynamics of a given situation. While not as directly abusive to persons as destructive humor, it does mask a fear of vulnerability or a reluctance to face conflict head-on and thus exacerbates the interpersonal difficulty.

> Upon his return from work, the husband is greeted by his wife who immediately attempts to discuss with him the teacher-parent conference at their son's school earlier that day. When she tells him the teacher expressed concern that the son is "goofing off," lethargic, and becoming irresponsible, the husband grins and responds, "So Jeff is acting like your side of the family again, huh?"

---

[8] "The Peacemakers," *Sermons At Crescent Hill Baptist Church* (Louisville, KY) 2:24 (19 June 1966).

He then switches on the T.V. to the football game already in progress, feeling he's won a temporary reprieve. He does not see the wife's clenched fists or sense the depth of the anger she is—for the present—repressing.

Another example:

The professor expresses concern that the student did not meet the deadline for an important assignment. With a disarming grin the student replies, "Well, nobody's perfect, Prof. I really tried to burn the midnight oil on that one, but I guess the fume musta got to me and I fell asleep!"

Humor can sometimes serve as a *denial* mechanism.

A patient with extreme facial disfigurement repeatedly remarks with a brittle laugh, "Well, I ain't never going to be no Clark Gable. That I know!"

Despite the attempt at joviality regarding his condition, he is depressed by the situation. Yet he appears unable to deal with the reality of it.

A related type of humor is *hostile*. Laughter or attempts at humor can actually be expressions of anger. Strong, repressed feelings are sometimes vented unexpectedly. Apparently the psuedohumorous overtones allow a person to ventilate what he perceives as unacceptable or even threatening feelings and behaviors.

Satirical humor is a type that is used to delineate the tension existing in the conflict between what *is* and what *ought to be*. It is humor used as a method of protest. Satire can be biting, astringent social comment or devastatingly accurate depictions of individual foibles. (George B. Shaw once advised, "If you want to tell people the truth, make them laugh or they will kill you.") Political cartoonists and some graffiti buffs make effective use of satire.

A more neutral type of humor is the *designed* type which involves a deliberate, calculated attempt to interrupt—"jar loose"—the thinking process of another. This consciously manipulative kind of humor can be raucous, slapstick, or simply laugh-evoking. Such laughter can prompt the act of slapping one's thigh in mirth, bending double, or simply inducing a smile which can cause changes in the muscular-skeletal arrangement and can afford a beneficial release.

Yet another type that is often seen by medical professionals is *bizarre* humor characterized by inappropriate laughter, excessive punning, and aberrant behavior intended to entertain as well as provide an "acting-out" arena. This extreme type of humor evidences a faulty approach to reality and the need for therapeutic intervention. V. H. Rosen describes obsessive-compulsive behavior in terms of twisted humor. Obsessive behaviors he calls "grotesque parodies without laughter" and compulsions "ritual travesties devoid of fun."[9]

Humor as a Tool: Diagnostic and Therapeutic

Physicians have long appreciated the efficacy of humor-response as a diagnostic tool. An inappropriate response to humor can be indicative of poor mental health. Humor strategy can serve as a trial balloon for testing the patient's capacity for spontaneity and self-exploration. It can help the patient to examine his own attitudes and actions both critically and realistically.

A humor history of the patient can be instructive. For example, what place did teasing have in the patient's early life? Did he hear laughter (other than television's canned soundtrack) in his early years at home? What kinds of jokes, comedies or cartoons does he prefer? Does he have a favorite joke? What was the most recent incident which caused this person to laugh?

The reappearance of appropriate responses to humor can indicate a reemergence from psychosis or illness. Howard Gardner, neuropsychological researcher at Boston University School of Medicine, maintains that "only when the brain's two hemispheres are working together can we appreciate the moral of a story, the meaning of a metaphor, words describing emotion and the punch line of a joke."[10]

Humor can serve with other diagnostic tools to give added insights into the patient's state of mind, social interaction and therapy needs.

A twenty-nine year old male suffering injuries from a severe automobile accident was referred to me by his psychia-

---

[9]"Variants of Cosmic Caricature and Their Relationship to Obsessive Compulsive Phenomena," *Journal of the American Psychiatric Association* 11:704 (1963).

[10]*Psychology today* 15:2 (February 1981): 74.

trist. Confined temporarily to a wheelchair, he had become despondent about his chances for recovery. Pale, rigid features and a furtive look in his eyes attested to his intense anxiety.

After introducing myself as a theological consultant, I sat down to talk with this patient. He was reluctant to engage in self-revealing dialogue until I quietly asked him, "Mike, what is your greatest fear?" Still without looking at me, he answered woodenly, "Death."

After a pause, I extended my hand to him in a "let's-shake-hands" gesture and said with a smile, "Join the club, buddy."

Mike hesitated, then grasped my hand, looked at me directly, and smiled. I commented that he'd expressed the universal fear of mankind, and we began the movement from generalities to specific focus.

Norman Cousins claims he found during his illness that ten minutes of genuine belly laughter had an anesthetic effect and would "give me at least two hours of pain-free sleep."[11] He also points out that "hearty laughter is a good way to jog internally without having to go outside."[12]

People are risible creatures, and like Ol' Br'er Rabbit, everyone needs a "laughing place," a space where we can laugh at ourselves, the world, and the ambiguities of life. Thus we can find refreshment via a clearer perspective of reality. This is sometimes referred to as psychical distancing, that is, the moving aside psychically from the event or situation so that reality testing and new insights can result. This psychic space aids in the expansion of consciousness. (The artistically gifted person utilizes this distancing with profound results.)

Humor can serve as a catalyst for changing affect and perception.

A sixty-seven-year old cultured woman, recently widowed, was referred to me because of her obsession with immediately dying. Defiantly she insisted, "I am going to die *today*. I've already made my prayers of contrition. No matter what anybody says, I am going to die this *very day!* I'm ready. I'm going this day to be with God! I'm going!"

---

[11]Cousins, *Anatomy of an Illness*, p. 39.

[12]Ibid., p. 85.

I took her hand, looked directly at her and said softly with a smile, "Now, my dear, don't you really think it would be better to wait for an invitation?"

She looked startled, then smiled and relaxed. "I guess you're right," she responded. "I'd never go where I'm not invited."

The therapeutic aspects of humor can aid hospitalized patients in coping with their loss of autonomy and control, their diminishing self-esteem and the seeming indignities of adjusting to institutional life. "Being on this psycho ward all these weeks is driving me crazy," asserts one patient. Another insists, "These shrinks are nuttier than all of us!" Thus the coping mechanisms are lubricated with the oil of laughter, though tinged with derision.

The Americans taken hostage in Iran in 1979 used humor to reduce the stress of forced confinement. Some of them nicknamed the windowless basement of the U.S. embassy in Tehran the "Mushroom Inn"; and one captive painted on his cell walls patriotic slogans in Spanish which the Iranians were unable to translate. These and other strategies helped the hostages to maintain a measure of defense against the psychic indignities inflicted by their captors.

The medical staff dealing with patients needs to be able to maintain a balance of humor along with care. One aide in a psychiatric ward confessed that staff members there do occasionally joke among themselves about their work. "If we weren't able to laugh sometimes," she said, "we'd be in tears most of the time!"

This same aide sought to make chart write-ups humorous as well as carefully explicit. On one chart she noted, "Patient at 2:15 A.M. requested to commit suicide. Request denied." The terse "request denied" became a catchword for the staff, affording an occasional chuckle in the midst of otherwise stressful situations.

This type of humor can evolve into a *gallows* humor which serves as an emotional buffer, enabling medical personnel to cope with the ghastliness and fatigue experienced in their daily tasks.

A female patient had attempted suicide by swallowing a massive dose of a corrosive drain cleaner. The hospital medical staff was able to restore her to functioning capacities after intensive work. On her chart someone noted, "Patient took an overdose of Drano." The staff began to ask each other jokingly, "What would constitute a *normal* dose?"

The M*A*S*H character "Hawkeye" depicts the sardonic, wry amusement of the person who can laugh at the aspects of both surgery and warfare. As a veteran of combat in Vietnam observed, "If I couldn't have laughed at what was happening all around me, I would have gone stark crazy. I laughed my way through it all."

While this type of safety-valve humor can be a healthy release for the medical professional, it does present the risk of alienating the patient or those closely related to the patient. Thus the ethical question arises, "How much is too much?" Where are the boundaries between protective emotional distance and the unsettling of others?

> Grieving parents requested that a pediatrician and theological consultant attend the autopsy to be performed on their recently deceased year-old infant. The father had worked as a carpenter on the hospital's scaffolding; therefore, he had, on occasion, overheard the laughter and jesting of the doctors as they performed autopsies. "I want you, a minister, to be there," he said, "so they won't handle my child irreverently."

Medical professionals need to develop moral sensitivity and discernment in balancing the need for levity with the vulnerability of other's feelings. Discreet humorous exchanges among staff members can serve as a model for patients in their own interpersonal encounters. But the staff needs to be acutely sensitive to the dynamics involved and strive to be supportive of each other as well as of the patients in their care.

In summary, there appear to be three basic principles inherent in the use of humor as a tool for patient diagnosis and care:
- Humor should lead to acceptance.
- Humor can be a means of engendering hope and support.
- Humor can provide enlightenment and insight through a shift in perspective and thus be beneficial.

The Ethics of Humor

Some practical ethical issues may stem from the use of humor as a therapeutic tool, especially in psychotherapy. Unethical humorizing may prove to be damaging to the physician- or therapist-patient relationship.

Lawrence Kubie holds that humor has an extremely limited as well as potentially destructive role in psychotherapy. He lists more than fifteen possibly destructive effects, all of which have ethical implications. Among these are: (1) attempting to seduce or "woo" the patient into liking and affirming the therapist; (2) a blocking of the patient's stream of feeling and thought by the therapist's humor; (3) using humor as a defense against the therapist's own anxiety and against those defenses of the patient; and (4) confusing the patient who wonders if the therapist is serious or just joking. These and other considerations make Kubie hesitate to use humor in therapy.[13]

I would stress Kubie's view that the physician and therapist must avoid confusing patients with the use of humor. Too often clients are left in doubt as to whether or not they are being taken seriously, or even whether or not to take their own illness seriously. Søren Kierkegaard's parable of "The Happy Conflagration" illustrates how people are some-times prone not to accept truth presented in a humorous context. According to this philosopher, a clown rushed onstage to inform the townspeople that a fire had broken out backstage and they all were in mortal danger. Because of his ludicrous costume as well as his frenzy, the audience thought this was part of his act and they applauded heartily. The more frantically the clown repeated his warning, the louder the crowd shouted and applauded.[14]

Of course, any form of humor which demeans the patient and de-stroys the I-Thou relationship between therapist and client is unethical. But the wise and mature therapist can avoid Kubie's destructive pitfalls of humor. A number of advocates of the use of humor in psychotherapy challenge Kubie and others reluctant to use humor as a therapeutic tool. Julius E. Heuscher, M.D., believes that humor can prove helpful when used judicially in psychotherapy.[15] He reflects the view of many other psychotherapists.[16]

---

[13]Lawrence S. Kubie, "The Destructive Potential of Humor in Psychotherapy," *The American Journal of Psychotherapy* 127:7 (January 1971): 861-66; cf. Theodore Reik, *Jewish Wit* (New York: Gamut Press, 1962).

[14]Søren Kierkegaard, *Either/Or*, trans. by Walter Lowrie (Princeton: Princeton University Press, 1944), 1:30.

[15]Julius E. Heuscher, "The Role of Humor and Folklore Themes in Psychotherapy," *The American Journal of Psychiatry* 137:12 (December 1980): 1546-49.

[16]Joseph Levine, "Humor as a Form of Therapy, in *It's a Funny Thing, Humour*, ed. by A. J. Chapman and H. C. Foot (Oxford, England: Pergamon Press, 1977); Marianne Ron-

To be ethical in therapist-patient relationships, humor must be spontaneous, sincere, and never at the expense of the patient, his relatives, friends, or other patients. It is not to be employed as a defensive mechanism by the therapist or as a means of manipulating a patient. The quality of humor utilized by the therapist should be that which will edify both therapist and client. For authentic humor is an instrument of agape-love which means to will the well-being of the other.

---

coli, "Bantering: A Therapeutic Strategy with Obsessional Patients," *Perspectives in Psychiatric Care* 12:4 (October-December 1974): 171-75; Eliyah Rosenheim, "Humor in Psychotherapy; An Interactive Experience," *American Journal of Psychiatry* 28:4 (October 1974): 584-91.

Epilogue

In this brief study I have dealt with only a few of the myriad moral problems in medicine. But comprehensive treatment of medical ethics was not intended. Rather, my purpose was to clarify the ground, criteria, and goal of ethics in relation to selected issues which confront the health care professional in daily practice. These issues include the emerging technological advances as well as the somewhat exotic ones of genetic engineering, surrogate parenting, and in vitro fertilization.

No ready-made, patent rules are available for application by the physician and other professionals to these increasingly complex issues. However, some basic guiding moral principles do exist. These principles are analogous to a compass—not a detailed roadmap—pointing in the direction of intelligent and imaginative moral action in the healing enterprise. (Many of these are articulated in the 1980 American Medical Association Code of Ethics.) Among these principles are the following:

- The health care professional must recognize the patient as a person to be treated with care and dignity.

- The health professional must be competent in his or her field and render competent service with compassion and respect for human dignity.

To these and the other principles of the AMA code I would add the principle of agape-love which is *to will and to work for the well-being of the other.*

All of the above guiding principles, along with others, are instruments implementing love for the health and happiness of the human person.

Bibliography

1. Related Readings

Chapter 1
Medical Ethics: An Overview

Edelstein, Ludwig, *Ancient Medicine.* Edited by Oswei Temkin and C. Lillian Temkin. Baltimore: Johns Hopkins University Press, 1967.

Jones, W. H. S. The Doctor's Oath: *An Essay in the History of Medicine.* Cambridge: The University Press, 1924.

King, Lester S. *The Medical World of the Eighteenth Century.* Chicago: University of Chicago Press, 1958.

Konold, Donald E. *A History of American Medical Ethics, 1847-1912.* Madison: State Historical Society of Wisconsin, 1962.

Percival, Thomas. *Percival's Medical Ethics.* Edited by Chauncey D. Leake. Huntington, N.Y.: R. E. Krieger Publishing Co., 1975.

Sigerist, Henry E. *A History of Medicine.* Two volumes. New York: Oxford University Press, 1951 and 1961.

Chapter 2
Moral Decision Making

(a)   Philosophical Ethics

Aiken, Henry. *Reason and Conduct.* New York: Alfred A. Knopf, 1962.

Dyck, Arthur J. *On Human Care: An Introduction to Ethics.* Nashville, Abingdon Press, 1977.

Frankena, William K. *Ethics*. Second Edition. Englewood Cliffs, NJ: Prentice-Hall, 1973.

MacIntyre, Alasdair. *A Short History of Ethics*. New York: Macmillan, 1966.

Quinton, A. M. *Utilitarian Ethics*. New York: St. Martin's Press, 1973.

Rawls, John. *A Theory of Justice*. Cambridge: Harvard University Press, 1971.

(b)   Theological Ethics

Fox, Marvin, editor. *Modern Jewish Ethics: Theory and Practice*. Columbus: Ohio State University Press, 1975.

Gustafson, James M. *Can Ethics Be Christian?* Chicago: University of Chicago Press, 1975.

―――― . *Theology and Christian Ethics*. Philadelphia: United Church Press, 1974.

Haring, Bernard. *The Law of Christ*. Three volumes. Philadelphia: Westminster Press, 1961, 1963, 1975.

Lehmann, Paul L. *Ethics in a Christian Context*. New York: Harper and Row, 1963.

McCormick, Richard A. *Ambiguity in Moral Choice*. Milwaukee: Marquette University Press, 1973.

Niebuhr, H. Richard. *Christ and Culture*. New York: Harper and Row, 1951.

Niebuhr, Reinhold. *An Interpretation of Christian Ethics*. Cleveland: The World Publishing Company, 1963. (Originally published 1935.)

Outka, Gene H. *Agape: An Ethical Analysis*. New Haven: Yale University Press, 1972.

―――― , and Paul Ramsey, editors. *Norm and Context in Christian Ethics*. New York: Charles Scribner's Sons, 1968.

Ramsey, Paul. *Basic Christian Ethics*. New York: Charles Scribner's Sons, 1950.

―――― . *Deeds and Rules in Christian Ethics*. New York: Charles Scribner's Sons, 1950.

Tillich, Paul. *Love, Power, and Justice*. New York: Oxford University Press, 1954.

Chapter 3
Ethics in Physician-Patient Relations

Barnette, Henlee. "The Psychiatric Patient As a Person." *Pastoral Psychology* 27:1 (Fall 1978): 39-48.

Branson, Roy, "The Secularization of American Medicine." *Hastings Center Report* 3:2 (1973): 17-28.

Cousins, Norman. *Anatomy of An Illness: As Perceived By The Patient*. New York: W. W. Norton and Co., 1979.

Leake, Chauncey D., editor. *Percival's Medical Ethics*. Hunting, NY: Robert E. Krieger Publishing Co., 1975.

Peabody, Francis. "The Care of the Patient." *Doctor and Patient*. New York: Macmillan Co., 1930.

Ramsey, Paul. *The Patient As A Person*. New Haven: Yale University Press, 1980.

Tournier, Paul. *The Healing of Persons*. New York: Harper and Row, 1965.

_____ . *The Meaning of Persons*. New York: Harper and Row, 1965.

Veatch, Robert M. "Models for Ethical Medicine in a Revolutionary Age." *The Hastings Center Report* 2:3 (1972): 5-6.

Chapter 4
Loneliness

Gordon, S. *Lonely in America*. New York: Simon and Schuster, 1976.

Keyes, R. *We, the Lonely People: Searching for Community*. New York: Harper and Row, 1973.

Lynch, J. J. *The Broken Heart: The Medical Consequences of Loneliness*. New York: Basic Books, 1977.

_____ , and W. H. Convey. "Loneliness, Disease, and Death: Alternative Approaches." *Psychosomatics* 20:10 (October 1979): 702-708.

Moustakas, C. E. *The Touch of Loneliness*. Englewood Cliffs, NJ: Prentice-Hall, 1972.

Niemi, T. "Effect of Loneliness on Mortality After Retirement." *Scandinavian Journal of Social Medicine* 7:2 (1979): 63-65.

Satran, G. "Notes on Loneliness." *Journal of the American Academy of Psychoanalysis* 6:3 (July 1978): 281-300.

Schultz, T. *Bittersweet: Surviving and Growing from Loneliness*. New York: Crowell, 1976.

Slater, P. *The Pursuit of Loneliness: American Culture at the Breaking Point*. Revised edition. Boston: Beacon Press, 1976.

Thauberger, P. C., and J. F. Cleveland. "Avoidance of Ontological Confrontation of Loneliness and Some Epidemilogical Indices of Social Behavior and Health," *Perceptual Motor Skills* (June 1979).

Tillich, Paul. *The Courage To Be*. New Haven: Yale University Press, 1952.

Tournier, Paul. *Escape From Loneliness*. Translated by John S. Gilmour. Philadelphia: Westminster Press, 1977.

Weiss, R. S. *Loneliness: The Experience of Emotional and Social Isolation*. Cambridge: MIT Press, 1973.

Chapter 5
Guilt

Freud, Sigmund. *Civilization and Its Discontents*. New York: W. W. Norton and Co., 1961.

_____ . *The Future of an Illusion*. New York: Liveright Publishing Corporation, 1949.

McKenzie, John C. *Guilt: Its Meaning and Significance*. London: George Allen and Unwin, 1962.

Menninger, Karl. *Whatever Became of Sin?* New York: Hawthorne Books, Inc., 1973.

Murphy, H. B. "The Advent of Guilt Feelings as a Common Depressive Symptom: A Historical Comparison on Two Continents." *Psychiatry* 41 (August 1978): 229-42.

Oden, Tom, *Guilt Free*. Nashville: Abingdon, 1980.

Shapiro, M. B. "The Relation of Guilt and Other Feelings to the Diagnosis of Depression." *British Journal of Medical Psychology* 52 (June 1979): 123-32.

Stein, Edward. *Guilt: Theory and Therapy*. Philadelphia: Westminster Press, 1968.

Chapter 6
Homosexuality

Acosta, F. X. "Etiology and Treatment of Homosexuality: A Review." *Archives of Sexual Behavior* 4:1 (January 1975): 9-29.

Austin, C. R. "Bisexuality and the Problem of Its Social Acceptance." *Journal of Medical Ethics* 4 (September 1978): 132-37.

Blumstein, P. W., and P. Schwartz, "Bisexuality in Women." *Archives of Sexual Behavior* 5 (March 1976): 171-81.

Brown, Howard. *Familiar Faces, Hidden Lives*. New York: Harcourt Brace Jovanovich, 1976.

Gittings, B. B. *A Gay Bibliography*. Philadelphia: Task Force on Gay Liberation, American Library Association, 1974.

Gross, M. J. "Changing Attitudes Toward Homosexuality." *Perspectives in Psychiatric Care* 16:2 (1978): 71-75.

Kanzer, M. "Freud's Views on Bisexuality and Therapy: Clinical Notes." *International Journal of Psychiatry* 10:4 (December 1972): 66-69.

Limentani, A. "The Differential Diagnosis of Homosexuality." *British Journal of Medical Psychology* 50:3 (September 1977): 209-16.

Masters, William H., and Virginia E. Johnson. *Homosexuality in Perspective*. Boston: Little, Brown and Co., 1979.

Pomeroy, Wardell. "Homosexuality," in Ralph Weltge, editor, *The Same Sex: An Appraisal of Homosexuality*. Philadelphia/Boston: Pilgrim Press, 1979. Pages 7-8.

Thomas, S. P. "Bisexuality: A Sexual Orientation of Great Diversity." *Journal of Psychiatric Nursing* 18:4 (April 1980): 19-27.

Tripp, C. A. *The Homosexual Matrix*. New York: McGraw-Hill Book Co., 1975. Page 9.

Chapter 7
In Vitro and Surrogate Motherhood

Bok, Sissela. "Ethical Problems of Abortion." *The Hastings Center Report* 2:1 (1974): 42.

"Pregnancy By Proxy." *Newsweek*, 7 July 1980, page 72.

Walters, Leroy. "Human in Vitro Fertilization: A Review of the Ethical Literature." *The Hastings Center Report* 9:4 (1979): 23-43.

Chapter 8
Genetic Engineering

Anderson, W. F., and J. C. Fletcher. "Gene Therapy in Human Beings: When Is It Ethical to Begin?" *New England Journal of Medicine* (November 1980): 1293-97.

Check, W. A. "How They Did It: The Synthesis of Interferon." *Journal of the American Medical Association* 243:8 (February 22-29): 721-22.

Eisenberg, Leon. "The Outcome as Cause: Predestination and Human Cloning." *Journal of Medicine and Philosophy* 1 (1976): 318-31.

Fletcher, John. "Moral and Ethical Problems of Pre-Natal Diagnosis." *Clinical Genetics* 8 (1975): 251-57.

Fletcher, Joseph. "Ethical Aspects of Genetic Controls." *New England Journal of Medicine* 285 (30 September 1971): 776-83.

Grobstein, Clifford. "The Recombinant-DNA Debate." *Scientific American* 237:7 (July 1977): 22-23.

Gunby, P. "Sex Selection Before Child's Conception." *Journal of the American Medical Association* 241:12 (23 March 1979): 1220-26.

Gustafson, James M. "Genetic Engineering and the Normative View of the Human," in *Ethical Issues in Biology and Medicine*, edited by Preston Williams, Cambridge, MA: Schenkman, 1972. Pages 46-58.

Johnson, R. S. "Gene Transfer Experiment in Humans Meets With Scant Approval." *Journal of the American Medical Association* 244:19 (November 1980): 2139-40.

Leder, P. "Recombinant DNA Technology: Prologue and Promise." *Radiology* 130:2 (February 1979): 289-92.

McCormack, M. K. "Medical Genetics and Family Practice." *American Family Physician* 20:3 (September 1979): 142-54.

Mercola, K. E., and M. J. Cline. "Sounding Boards. The Potentials of Inserting New Genetic Information." *New England Journal of Medicine* 303:22 (27 November 1980): 1297-1300.

Milutinovic, J., et al: "Autosomal Dominant Polycystic Kidney Disease: Early Diagnosis and Data for Genetic Counselling." *Lancet* 2 (7 June 1980): 1203-1206.

Powledge, Tabitha M. "Prenatal Diagnosis: Now the Problems." *New Scientist* 69:987 (12 February 1978): 332-34.

———— , D. Callahan, and K. Dismukes. "Splicing Genes." *Hastings Center Report* 7 (April 1977): 18-30.

Riccardi, Vincent M. "Health Care and Disease Prevention Through Genetic Counseling: A Regional Approach." *American Journal of Public Health* 66 (March 1976): 268-72.

Sperber, Michael A., and Lissy F. Jarvik, editors. *Psychiatry and Genetics: Psychosocial, Ethical, and Legal Considerations.* New York: Basic Books, 1976.

Wilson, Edward. *On Human Nature.* Cambridge: Harvard University Press, 1978.

Witkin, Herman A., et al. "Criminality in XYY Man: Do Criminals Really Have Abnormal Genes?" *Science Digest* 79 (January 1976): 33-38.

Chapter 9
Communicating In Extremis

Bok, Sissela. *Lying: Moral Choices in Public and Private Life.* New York: Pantheon Books, 1978.

Hinkle, B. J. "Living With the Demands of Confidentiality." *Journal of Legal Medicine* 5 (January 1977): 9-14.

Jospe, Michael. *The Placebo Effect in Healing.* Lexington, MA: Lexington Books, 1978.

Oken, Donald. "What to Tell Cancer Patients." *Journal of the American Medical Association* 175 (1 April 1961): 1120-28.

Peck, Arthur. "Emotional Reactions to Having Cancer." *CA—Cancer Journal for Physicians* 22 (September-October 1972): 284-91.

Rea, M. Priscilla, et al. "Physicians and the Terminal Patient: Some Selected Attitudes and Behavior." *Omega* 6 (1975): 291-302.

Roth, L. H., et al. "Dangerousness, Confidentiality, and the Duty to Warn." *American Journal of Psychiatry* 134 (March 1977): 508-11.

Rozovsky, Lorne Elkin, and Syed Naveed Akhtar. "Should Psychiatric Communication Be Privileged." *Legal Medical Quarterly* 1 (June 1977): 115-18.

Siegler, Mark. "Pascal's Wager and the Hanging of Crepe." *New England Journal of Medicine* 293 (23 October 1975): 853-57.

Chapter 10
Suicide

Alvarez, A. *The Savage God: A Study of Suicide.* New York: Random House, 1972.

Beck, Aaron T., et al. "Classification of Suicidal Behaviors: II. Dimensions of Suicidal Intent." *Archives of General Psychiatry* 33 (July 1976): 835-37.

Cohen-Sandler, R. and A. L. Berman. "Diagnosis and Treatment of Childhood Depression and Self-Destructive Behavior." *Journal of Family Practice* 11:1 (July 1980): 51-58.

Ennis, J. and R. Barnes. "More on Suicide and Women Physicians." *American Journal of Psychiatry* 137:9 (September 1980): 1125-26.

Farberow, N. L. and Shneidman, E. S., editors. *The Cry For Help.* New York: McGraw-Hill, 1961.

Hewett, John H., *After Suicide.* Philadelphia: Westminster Press, 1980.

Modlin, H. C. "Management of Suicidal Behavior," *Rhode Island Medical Journal* 63:4 (April 1980).

Paulson, M. J., D. Stone, and R. Sposto. "Suicide Potential and Behavior in Children Ages 4 to 12." *Suicide and Life-Threatening Behavior* 8:4 (Winter 1978): 225-42.

Perlin, Seymour. *A Handbook for the Study of Suicide.* New York: Oxford University Press, 1975.

Phillips, D. P., and J. Liu. "The Frequency of Suicides Around Major Public Holidays: Some Surprising Findings." *Suicide and Life-Threatening Behavior* 10:1 (Spring 1980): 41-50.

Portwood, Doris. *Common Sense Suicide: The Final Right.* New York: Dodd, Mead, and Co., 1978.

Pretzel, P. W. "Philosophical and Ethical Considerations of Suicide Prevention." *Bulletin of Suicidology* (July 1968): 30-38.

Rich, C. L., and F. N. Pitts, Jr. "Suicide by Psychiatrists: A Study of Medical Specialists Among 18,730 Consecutive Physician Deaths During a Five-Year Period, 1967-72." *Journal of Clinical Psychiatry* 41:8 (August 1980): 261-63.

Slater, Eliot. "Assisted Suicide: Some Ethical Considerations." *International Journal of Health Services* 6 (1976): 321-30.

Szasz, Thomas S. "The Ethics of Suicide." *The Antioch Review* 31 (Spring 1971): 7-17.

Waltzer, H. "Malpractice Liability in a Patient's Suicide." *American Journal of Psychotherapy* 34:1 (January 1980): 89-98.

Chapter 11
Death

Becker, Ernest. *The Denial of Death.* New York: The Free Press, 1973.

Behnke, John A., and Sissela Bok. *The Dilemmas of Euthanasia.* New York: Doubleday Anchor, 1975.

Caughill, Rita E., editor. *The Dying Patient: A Supportive Approach.* Boston: Little, Brown and Co., 1977.

Horan, Dennis J., and David Mall, editors. *Death, Dying, and Euthanasia.* Washington, DC: University Publications of America, 1977.

Ross, Elisabeth. *Death: The Final Stage of Growth.* Englewood Cliffs, NJ: Prentice-⹍ ⹍, 1975.

_____ . *On Death and Dying.* New York: Macmillan, 1969.

Mack, Arien, editor. *Death in the American Experience.* New York: Schocken Books, 1973.

Maguire, Daniel C. *Death By Choice.* New York: Doubleday, 1974.

Oden, Thomas C. *Should Treatment Be Terminated? Moral Guidelines for Christian Families and Pastors.* New York: Harper and Row, 1976.

Pattison, E. Mansel. *The Experience of Dying.* Englewood Cliffs, NJ: Prentice-Hall, 1977.

Riemer, Jack, editor. *Jewish Reflections on Death.* New York: Schocken Books, 1975.

Szasz, Thomas S. "The Ethics of Suicide." *The Antioch Review* 31 (Spring 1971): 7-17.

Schulz, Richard, and David Aderman. "How the Medical Staff Copes with Dying Patients: A Critical Review." *Omega* 7:1 (1976): 11-21.

Steinfels, Peter, and Robert M. Veatch, editors. *Death Inside Out.* New York: Harper and Row, 1975.

Troup, Stanley B., and William A. Greene, editors. *The Patient, Death, and the Family.* New York: Charles Scribner's Sons, 1974.

Veatch, Robert M., *Death, Dying, and the Biological Revolution.* New Haven: Yale University Press, 1976.

————. "Caring for the Dying Person—Ethical Issues at Stake." In *Dying and Death: A Clinical Guide for Caregivers*, edited by David Barton. Baltimore: The Williams and Wilkins Company, 1977. Pages 150-69.

Veith, Frank J., et al. "Brain Death." Part 1. "A Status Report of Medical and Ethical Consideration"; and Part 2, "A Status Report of Legal Considerations." *Journal of the American Medical Association* 238 (October 10 and 17): 1651-55 and 1744-48.

Weir, Robert F., editor. *Ethical Issues in Death and Dying.* New York: Columbia University, 1977.

Chapter 12
Humor

Chapman, A. J. and H. C. Foot, editors. *It's a Funny Thing, Humor.* Oxford, England: Pergamon Press, 1977.

Coates, J. F., "Wit and Humor: A Neglected Aid in Crowd and Mob Control." *Crime and Delinquency* 18 (1972): 184-91.

Cousins, Norman. *Anatomy of an Illness.* New York: W. W. Norton and Co., 1979.

Freud, Sigmund. *Jokes and Their Relation to the Unconscious.* New York: W. W. Norton and Co., Inc., 1960.

Heuscher, Julius E. "The Role of Humor and Folklore Themes in Psychotherapy." *The American Journal of Psychiatry* 137:12 (December 1980): 1546-49.

Kubie, Lawrence S. "The Destructive Potential of Humor in Psychotherapy." *The American Journal of Psychotherapy* 127:7 (January 1971): 861-66.

Moody, Raymond. *Laugh After Laugh: The Healing Power of Humor.* Jacksonville, FL: Headwaters Press, 1978.

Reik, Theodore, *Jewish Wit.* New York: Gamut Press, 1962.

Roncoli, Marianne. "Bantering: A Therapeutic Strategy with Obsessional Patients," *Perspectives in Psychiatric Care* 12:4 (October-December, 1974): 171-75.

Rosenheim, Eliyah. "Humor in Psychotherapy: An Interactive Experience." *American Journal of Psychiatry* 28:4 (October 1974): 584-91.

Walsh, James J. *Laughter and Health.* New York: D. Appleton and Co., 1928.

2. General Works

Brody, Howard. *Ethical Decisions in Medicine.* Boston: Little, Brown and Company, 1976.

Campbell, A. V. *Moral Dilemmas in Medicine.* Baltimore: The Williams and Wilkins Co., 1972.

Curran, Charles E. *Politics, Medicine and Christian Ethics.* Philadelphia: Fortress Press, 1973.

Duncan, A. S., G. R. Dunstan, and R. B. Wellbourn. *Dictionary of Medical Ethics.* London: Darton, Longman and Todd, 1977.

Fletcher, Joseph. *Morals and Medicine*. Boston: Beacon Press, 1954.

Gustafson, James M. *The Contributions of Theology to Medical Ethics*. 1975 Pere Marquette Theology Lecture. Milwaukee: Marquette University Theology Department, 1975.

Haring, Bernard. *Ethics of Manipulation: Issues in Medicine, Behavior Control and Genetics*. New York: The Seabury Press, 1975.

_____. *Medical Ethics*. Notre Dame, IN: Fides Publishers, 1973.

Hollis, Harry, editor. *A Matter of Life and Death: Christian Perspectives*. Nashville: Broadman Press, 1977.

Jakobovits, Immanuel. *Jewish Medical Ethics*. New York: Bloch Publishing Co., 1959.

McCormick, Richard A. *Ambiguity in Moral Choice*. Milwaukee: Marquette University Press, 1973.

Nelson, James B. *Human Medicine: Ethical Perspectives on New Medical Issues*. Minneapolis: Augsburg Publishing House, 1973.

Ramsey, Paul. *Ethics at the Edges of Life: Medical and Legal Intersections*. New Haven: Yale University Press, 1978.

Reiser, Stanley Joel, Arthur J. Dyck, and William J. Curran, editors. *Ethics in Medicine: Historical Perspectives and Contemporary Concerns*. Cambridge: The M.I.T. Press, 1977.

Rosner, Fred. *Modern Medicine and Jewish Law*. New York: Yeshiva University Press, 1972.

Veatch, Robert M. *Case Studies in Medical Ethics*. Cambridge: Harvard University Press, 1977.

3. Journals

The American Journal of Medicine.
666 Fifth Ave., New York, NY 10019.

American Journal of Nursing.
555 West 57th St., New York, NY 10019.

The American Journal of Psychiatry.
1700 Eighteenth St., N. W., Washington, DC 20009.

The American Journal of Psychotherapy.
1268 East 84th St., Brooklyn, NY 11236.

British Medical Journal.
Tavistock Square, London, England.

Canadian Medical Association Journal.
1867 Alta Vista Dr., P.O. Box 8650, Ottawa, Ontario.

Comprehensive Psychiatry.
111 Fifth Ave., New York, NY 10003.

Ethics in Science and Medicine.
Pergamon Press, Maxwell House, Fairview Park, Elmsford, NY 10523.

The Hastings Center Report (formerly *Hastings Center Studies*).
Institute of Society, Ethics, and Life Sciences, 623 Warburton Ave., Hastings-on-Hudson, NY 10706.

Journal of the American Academy of Child Psychiatry.
92A Yale Station, New Haven, CT 06520.

The Journal of the American Medical Association.
535 North Dearborn St., Chicago, IL 60610.

The Journal of the Kentucky Medical Association.
3532 Ephraim McDowell Drive, Louisville, KY 40205.

Journal of Medical Ethics.
Society for the Study of Medical Ethics, Tavistock House East, Tavistock Square, London WC1H 9Lg.

Journal of Psychiatric Nursing and Mental Health Services.
6900 Grove Road, Thorofare, NJ 08086.

New England Journal of Medicine.
10 Shattuck St., Boston, MA 02115.

Pastoral Psychology.
Human Sciences Press, 72 Fifth Ave., New York, NY 10011.

RN.
Oradell, NJ 97649.

Appendixes

Appendix A

1. Oath of Hippocrates
(Sixth Century B.C.—First Century A.D.)

I swear by Apollo Physician and Aesculapius and Hygeia and Panacea and all the gods and goddesses, making them my witnesses, that I will fulfill according to my ability and judgment this oath and this covenant:

To hold him who has taught me this art as equal to my parents and to live my life in partnership with him, and if he is in need of money to give him a share of mine, and to regard his offspring as equal to my brothers in male lineage and to teach them this art—if they desire to learn it—without fee and covenant; to give a share of precepts and oral instruction and all the other learning to my sons and to the sons of him who has instructed me to pupils who have signed the covenant and have taken an oath according to the medical law, but to no one else.

I will apply dietetic measures for the benefit of the sick according to my ability and judgment; I will keep them from harm and injustice.

I will neither give a deadly drug to anybody if asked for it, nor will I make a suggestion to this effect. Similarly I will not give to a woman an abortive remedy. In purity and holiness I will guard my life and my art.

I will not use the knife, not even on sufferers from stone, but will withdraw in favor of such men as are engaged in this work.

Whatever houses I may visit, I will come for the benefit of the sick, remaining free of all intentional injustice, of all mischief and in particular of sexual relations with both female and male persons, be they free or slaves.

What I may see or hear in the course of the treatment or even outside of the treatment in regard to the life of men, which on no account one must spread abroad, I will keep to myself holding such things shameful to be spoken about.

If I fulfill this oath and do not violate it, may it be granted to me to enjoy life and art, being honored with fame among all men for all time to come; if I transgress it and swear falsely, may the opposite of all this be my lot.

(Ludwig Edelstein, "The Hippocratic Oath: Text, Translation and Interpretation," *Bulletin of the History of Medicine*, Supplement 1 [Baltimore: Johns Hopkins Press, 1943], p. 3. Reprinted with the permission of the Johns Hopkins University Press.)

2. Daily Prayer of a Physician
(Also called "Prayer of Moses Maimonides")

Almighty God, Thou has created the human body with infinite wisdom. Ten thousand times ten thousand organs hast Thou combined in it that act unceasingly and harmoniously to preserve the whole in all its beauty—the body which is the envelope of the immortal soul. They are ever acting in perfect order, agreement and accord. Yet, when the frailty of matter or the unbridling of passions deranges this order or interrupts this accord, then forces clash and the body crumbles into the primal dust from which it came. Thou sendest to man diseases as beneficent messengers to foretell approaching danger and to urge him to avert it.

Thou hast blest Thine earth, Thy rivers and Thy mountains with healing substances; they enable Thy creatures to alleviate their sufferings and to heal their illnesses. Thou hast endowed man with the wisdom to relieve the suffering of his brother, to recognize his disorders, to extract the healing substances, to discover their powers and to prepare and to apply them to suit every ill. In Thine Eternal Providence Thou hast chosen me to watch over the life and health of Thy creatures. I am now about to apply myself to the duties of my profession. Support me, Almighty God, in these great labors that they may benefit mankind for without Thy help not even the least thing will succeed.

Inspire me with love for my art and for Thy creatures. Do not allow thirst for profit, ambition for renown and admiration, to interfere with my profession, for these are the enemies of truth and of love for mankind and they can lead astray in the great task of attending to the welfare of Thy creatures. Preserve the strength of my body and of my soul that they ever be ready to cheerfully help and support rich and poor, good and bad, enemy as well as friend. In the sufferer let me see only the human being. Illumine my mind that it recognize what presents itself and that it may comprehend what is absent or hidden. Let it not fail to see what is visible, but do not permit it to arrogate to itself the power to see what cannot be seen, for delicate and indefinite are the bounds of the great art of caring for the lives and health of Thy creatures. Let me never be absent-minded. May no strange thoughts divert my attention at the bedside of the sick, or disturb my mind in its silent labors, for great and sacred are the thoughtful deliberations required to preserve the lives and health of Thy creatures.

Grant that my patients have confidence in me and my art and follow my directions and my counsel. Remove from their midst all charlatans and the host of officious relatives and know-all nurses, cruel people who arrogantly frustrate the wisest purposes of our art and often lead Thy creatures to their death.

Should those who are wiser than I wish to improve and instruct me, let my soul gratefully follow their guidance; for vast is the extent of our art. Should conceited fools, however, censure me, then let love for my profession steel me against them, so that I remain steadfast without regard for age, for reputation, or for honor, because surrender would bring to Thy creatures sickness and death.

Imbue my soul with gentleness and calmness when older colleagues, proud of their age, wish to displace me or to scorn me or disdainfully to teach me. May even this be of advantage to me, for they know many things of which I am ignorant, but let not their arrogance give me pain. For they are old and old age is not master of the passions. I also hope to attain old age upon this earth, before Thee, Almighty God!

Le me be contented in everything except in the great science of my profession. Never allow the thought to arise in me that I have attained to sufficient knowledge, but vouchsafe to me the strength, the leisure and the ambition ever to extend my knowledge. For art is great, but the mind of man is ever expanding.

Almighty God! Thou has chosen me in Thy mercy to watch over the life and death of Thy creatures. I now apply myself to my profession. Support me in this great task so that it may benefit mankind, for without Thy help not even the least thing will succeed.

(Translated by Harry Friedenwald. *Bulletin of the Johns Hopkins Hospital* 28 [1917]: 260-61.)

3. Ethical and Religious Directives
for Catholic Health Facilities
(United States Catholic Conference, 1971)

I. General

1. The procedures listed in these Directives as permissable require at least implied or reasonably presumed, of the patient or his guardians. This condition is to be understood in all cases.

2. No person may be obliged to take part in a medical or surgical procedure which he judges in conscience to be immoral; nor may a health facility or any of its staff be obliged to provide a medical or surgical procedure which violates their conscience or these Directives.

3. Every patient, regardless of the extent of his physical or psychic disability, has a right to be treated with a respect consonant with his dignity as a person.

4. Man has the right and the duty to protect the integrity of his body together with all of its bodily functions.

5. Any procedure potentially harmful to the patient is morally justified only insofar as it is designed to produce a proportionate good.

6. Ordinarily the proportionate good that justifies a medical or surgical procedure should be the total good of the patient himself.

7. Adequate consultation is recommended, not only when there is doubt concerning the morality of some procedure, but also with regard to all procedures involving serious consequences, even though such procedures are listed here as permissible. The health facility has the right to insist on such consultations.

8. Everyone has the right and the duty to prepare for the solemn moment of death. Unless it is clear, therefore, that a dying patient is already well-prepared for death as regards both spiritual and temporal affairs, it is the physician's duty to inform him of his critical condition or to have some other responsible person impart this information.

9. The obligation of professional secrecy must be carefully fulfilled not only as regards the information on the patient's charts and records but also as regards confidential matters learned in the exercise of professional duties. Moreover, the charts and records must be duly safeguarded against inspection by those who have no right to see them.

10. The directly intended termination of any patient's life, even at his own request, is always morally wrong.

11. From the moment of conception, life must be guarded with the greatest care. Any deliberate medical procedure, the purpose of which is to deprive a fetus or an embryo of its life, is immoral.

12. Abortion, that is, the directly intended termination of pregnancy before viability, is never permitted nor is the directly intended destruction of a viable fetus. Every procedure whose sole immediate effect is the termination of pregnancy before viability is an abortion, which, in its moral context, includes the interval between conception and implantation of the embryo.

13. Operations, treatments, and medications, which do not directly intend termination of pregnancy but which have as their purpose the cure of a proportionately serious pathological condition of the mother, are permitted when they cannot be safely postponed until the fetus is viable, even though they may or will result in the death of the fetus. If the fetus is not certainly dead, it should be baptized.

14. Regarding the treatment of hemorrhage during pregnancy and before the fetus is viable: Procedures that are designed to empty the uterus of a living fetus still effectively attached to the mother are not permitted; procedures designed to stop hemorrhage (as distinguished from those designed precisely to expel the living and attached fetus) are permitted insofar as necessary, even if fetal death is inevitably a side effect.

15. Caesarean section for the removal of a viable fetus is permitted, even with risk to the life of the mother, when necessary for successful delivery. It is likewise permitted, even with risk to the child, when necessary for the safety of the mother.

16. In extrauterine pregnancy the dangerously affected part of the mother (for example, cervix, ovary, or fallopian tube) may be removed, even though fetal death is foreseen, provided that:

   a. the affectd part is presumed already to be so damaged and dangerously affected as to warrant its removal, and that

   b. the operation is not just a separation of the embryo or fetus from its site within the part (which would be a direct abortion from a uterine appendage), and that

   c. the operation cannot be postponed without notably increasing the danger to the mother.

17. Hysterectomy, in the presence of pregnancy and even before viability, is permitted when directed to the removal of a dangerous pathological condition of the uterus of such serious nature that the operation cannot be safely postponed until the fetus is viable.

II. Procedures Involving Reproductive Organs and Functions

18. Sterilization, whether permanent or temporary, for men or for women, may not be used as a means of contraception.

19. Similarly excluded is every action which, either in anticipation of the conjugal act, or in its accomplishment, or in the development of its natural consequences, proposes, whether as an end or as a means, to render procreation impossible.

20. Procedures that induce sterility, whether permanent or temporary, are permitted when: (a) they are immediately directed to the cure, diminution, or prevention of a serious pathological condition and are not directly contraceptive (that is, contraception is not the purpose); and (b) a simpler treatment is not reasonably available. Hence, for example, oophorectomy or irradiation of the ovaries may be allowed in treating carcinoma of the breast and metastasis therefrom; and orchidectomy is permitted in the treatment of a carcinoma of the prostate.

21. Because the ultimate personal expression of conjugal love in the marital act is

viewed as the only fitting context for the human sharing of the divine act of creation, donor insemination and insemination that is totally artificial are morally objectionable. However, help may be given to a normally performed conjugal act to attain its purpose. The use of the sex faculty outside the legitimate use by married partners is never permitted even for medical or other laudable purpose, for example, masturbation as a means of obtaining seminal specimens.

22. Hysterectomy is permitted when it is sincerely judged to be a necessary means of removing some serious uterine pathological condition. In these cases, the pathological condition of each patient must be considered individually and care must be taken that a hysterectomy is not performed merely as a contraceptive measure, or as a routine procedure after any definite number of Cesarean sections.

23. For a proportionate reason, labor may be induced after the fetus is viable.

24. In all cases in which the presence of pregnancy would render some procedure illicit (for example, curettage), the physician must make use of such pregnancy tests and consultation as may be needed in order to be reasonably certain that the patient is not pregnant. It is to be noted that curettage of the endometrium after rape to prevent implantation of a possible embryo is morally equivalent to abortion.

25. Radiation therapy of the mother's reproductive organs is permitted during pregnancy only when necessary to suppress a dangerous pathological condition.

III. Other Procedures

26. Therapeutic procedures which are likely to be dangerous are morally justifiable for proportionate reasons.

27. Experimentation on patients without due consent is morally objectionable, and even the moral right of the patient to consent is limited by his duties of stewardship.

28. Euthanasia ("mercy killing") in all its forms is forbidden. The failure to supply the ordinary means of preserving life is equivalent to euthanasia. However, neither the physician nor the patient is obliged to use extraordinary means.

29. It is not euthanasia to give a dying person sedatives and analgesics for the alleviation of pain, when such a measure is judged necessary, even though they may deprive the patient of the use of reason, or shorten his life.

30. The transplantation of organs from living donors is morally permissible when the anticipated benefit to the recipient is proportionate to the harm done to the donor, provided that the loss of such organ(s) does not deprive the donor of life itself nor of the functional integrity of his body.

31. Post-mortem examinations must not be begun until death is morally certain. Vital organs, that is, organs necessary to sustain life, may not be removed until death has taken place. The determination of the time of death must be made in accordance with responsible and commonly accepted scientific criteria. In accordance with current medical practice, to prevent any conflict of interest, the dying patient's doctor or doctors should ordinarily be distinct from the transplant team.

32. Ghost surgery, which implies the calculated deception of the patient as to the identity of the operation surgeon, is morally objectionable.

33. Unnecessary procedures, whether diagnostic or therapeutic, are morally objectionable. A procedure is unnecessary when no proportionate reason justifies it. A fortiori, any procedure that is contra-indicated by sound medical standards is unnecessary.

Appendix B

Patient's Bill of Rights

The American Hospital Association presents a Patient's Bill of Rights with the expectation that observance of these rights will contribute to more effective patient care and greater satisfaction for the patient, his physician, and the hospital organization. Further, the Association presents these rights in the expectation that they will be supported by the hospital on behalf of its patients, as an integral part of the healing process. It is recognized that a personal relationship between the physician and the patient is essential for the provision of proper medical care. The traditional physician-patient relationship takes on a new dimension when care is rendered within an organizational structure. Legal precedent has established that the institution itself also has a responsibility to the patient. It is in recognition of these factors that these rights are affirmed.

1. The patient has the right to considerate and respectful care.

2. The patient has the right to obtain from his physician complete current information concerning his diagnosis, treatment, and prognosis in terms the patient can be reasonably expected to understand. When it is not medically advisable to give such information to the patient, the information should be made available to an appropriate person in his behalf. He has the right to know by the name, the physician responsible for coordinating his care.

3. The patient has the right to receive from his physician information necessary to give informed consent prior to the start of any procedure and/or treatment. Except in emergencies, such information for informed consent, should include but not necessarily be limited to the specific procedure and/or treatment, the medically significant risks involved, and the probably duration of incapacitation. Where medically significant alternatives for care or treatment exist, or when the patient requests information concerning medical alternatives, the patient has the right to such information. The patient also has the right to such information. The patient also has the right to know the name of the person responsible for the procedures and/or treatment.

4. The patient has the right to refuse treatment to the extent permitted by law, and to be informed of the medical consequences of his action.*

5. The patient has the right to every consideration of his privacy concerning his own medical care program. Case discussion, consultation, examination, and treatment are confidential and should be conducted discreetly. Those not directly involved in his care must have the permission of the patient to be present.

6. The patient has the right to expect that all communications and records pertaining to his care should be treated as confidential.

7. The patient has the right to expect that within its capacity a hospital must make reasonable response to the request of a patient for services. The hospital must provide evaluation, service, and/or referral as indicated by the urgency of the case. When medically permissible a patient may be transferred to another facility only after he has received complete information and explanation concerning the needs for and alternatives to such a transfer. The institution to which the patient is to be transferred must first have accepted the patient for transfer.

8. The patient has the right to obtain information as to any relationship of his hospital to other health care and educational institutions insofar as his care is concerned. The patient has the right to obtain information as to the existence of any professional relationships among individuals, by name, who are treating him.

9. The patient has the right to be advised if the hospital proposes to engage in or

perform human experimentation affecting his care or treatment. The patient has the right to refuse to participate in such research projects.*

10. The patient has the right to expect reasonable continuity of care. He has the right to know in advance what appointment times and physicians are available and where. The patient has the right to expect that the hospital will provide a mechanism whereby he is informed by his physician or a delegate of the physician of the patient's continuing health care requirements following discharge.

11. The patient has the right to examine and receive an explanation of his bill regardless of source of payment.

12. The patient has the right to know what hospital rules and regulations apply to his conduct as a patient.

*No catalogue of rights can guarantee for the patient the kind of treatment he has a right to expect. A hospital has many functions to perform, including the prevention and treatment of disease, the education of both health professionals and patients, and the conduct of clinical research. All these activities must be conducted with an overriding concern for the patient, and, above all, the recognition of his dignity as a human being. Success in achieving this recognition assures success in the defense of the rights of the patient.

Appendix C
Ad Hoc Committee Definition of Brain Death

An organ, brain or other, that no longer functions and has no possibility of functioning again is for all practical purposes dead. Our first problem is to determine the characteristics of a permanently nonfunctioning brain.

A patient in this state appears to be in deep coma. The condition can be satisfactorily diagnosed by points 1, 2, and 3 to follow. The electroencephalogram (point 4) provides confirmatory data, and when available it should be utilized. In situations where for one reason or another, electroencephalographic monitoring is not available, the absence of cerebral function has to be determined by purely clinical signs, to be described, or by absence of circulation as judged by standstill of blood in the retinal vessels, or by absence of cardiac activity.

1. Unreceptivity and Unresponsitivity.—There is a total unawareness to externally applied stimuli and inner need and complete unresponsiveness—our definition of irreversible coma. Even the most intensely painful stimuli evoke no vocal or other response, not even a groan, withdrawal of a limb, or quickening of respiration.

2. No Movements or Breathing.—Observations covering a period of at least one hour by physicians is adequate to satisfy the criteria of no spontaneous muscular movements or spontaneous respiration or response to stimuli such as pain, touch, sound, or light. After the patient is on a mechanical respirator, the total absence of spontaneous breathing may be established by turning off the respirator for three minutes and observing whether there is any effort on the part of the subject to breathe spontaneously. (The respirator may be turned off for this time provided that at the start of the trial period the patient's carbon dioxide tension is within the normal range, and provided also that the patient had been breathing room air for at least 10 minutes prior to the trial.)

3. No reflexes.—Irreversible coma with abolition of central nervous system activity is evidenced in part by the absence of elicitable reflexes. The pupil will be fixed and dilated and will not respond to a direct source of bright light. Since the establishment of a fixed, dilated pupil is clear-cut in clinical practice, there should be no uncertainty as to its presence. Ocular movement (to head turning and to irrigation of the ears with ice water) and blinking are absent. There is no evidence of postural activity (decerebrate or other). Swallowing, yawning, vocalization are in abeyance. Corneal and pharyngeal reflexes are absent.

As a rule the stretch of tendon reflexes cannot be elicited; for example, tapping the tendons of the biceps, triceps, and pronator muscles, quadriceps and gastrocnemius muscles with the reflex hammer elicits no contraction of the respective muscles. Plantar or noxious stimulation gives no response.

4. Flat Electroencephalogram.—Of great confirmatory value is the flat or isoelectric EEG. We must assume that the electrodes have been properly applied, that the apparatus is functioning normally, and that the personnel in charge is competent. We consider it prudent to have one channel of the apparatus used for an electrocardiogram. This channel will monitor the ECG so that, if it appears in the electroencephalographic leads because of high resistance, it can be readily identified. It also establishes the presence of the active heart in the absence of the EEG. We recommend that another channel be used for a noncephalic lead. This will pick up space-borne or vibration-borne artifacts and identify them. The simplest form of such a monitoring noncephalic electrode has two leads over the dorsum of the hand, preferably the right hand, so the ECG will be minimal or absent. Since one of the requirements of this state is that there be no muscle activity, these two dorsal hand electrodes will not be bothered by muscle artifact. The apparatus should be run at standard gains 10μv/mm, 50μv/5 mm. Also it should be isoelectric at double this standard gain which is 5μv/mm or 25μv/5 mm. At least ten full minutes of recording are desirable, but twice that would be better.

It is also suggested that the gains at some point be opened to their full simplitude for a brief period (5 to 100 seconds) to see what is going on. Usually in an intensive care unit artifacts will dominate the picture, but these are readily identifiable. There shall be no electroencephalographic response to noise or to pinch.

All of the above tests shall be repeated at least 24 hours later with no change.

The validity of such data as indications of irreversible cerebral damage depends on the exclusion of two conditions: hypothermia (temperature below 90 F (32.2 C) or central nervous system depressants, such as barbiturates.*

*(Ad Hoc Committee of the Harvard Medical School to Examine the Definition of Brain Death, *"A Definition of Irreversible Coma," The Journal of The American Medical Association* 205 [1968]:337.)

Appendix D
*A Living Will**

TO MY FAMILY, MY PHYSICIAN, MY LAWYER, MY CLERGYMAN
TO ANY MEDICAL FACILITY IN WHOSE CARE I HAPPEN TO BE
TO ANY INDIVIDUAL WHO MAY BECOME RESPONSIBLE FOR MY HEALTH,
WELFARE OR AFFAIRS

Death is as much a reality as birth, growth, maturity and old age—it is the one certainty of life. If the time comes when I, _____ _____ _____ can no longer take part in decisions for my own future, let this statement stand as an expression of my wishes, while I am still of sound mind.

If the situation should arise in which there is no reasonable expectation of my recovery from physical or mental disability, I request that I be allowed to die and not be kept alive by artificial means or "heroic measures." I do not fear death itself as much as the indignities of deterioration, dependence and hopeless pain. I, therefore, ask that medication be mercifully administered to me to alleviate suffering even though this may hasten the moment of death.

This request is made after careful consideration. I hope you who care for me will feel morally bound to follow its mandate. I recognize that this appears to place a heavy responsibility upon you, but it is with the intention of relieving you of such responsibility and of placing it upon myself in accordance with my strong convictions, that this statement is made.

Signed _____

Date _____

Witness _____

Witness _____

Copies of this request have been given to _____

_____

_____

*Copies of A Living Will may be had from the Euthanasia Educational Council in New York City.

Index

EXPLORING MEDICAL ETHICS

Composition was by Mercer Press Services, Macon, Georgia:
designed by Jane Denslow,
the text was typeset by Janet Middlebrooks
on an Addressograph Multigraph Comp/Set Phototypesetter 5404,
and paginated on an A/M Comp/Set 4510.

Design and production specifications:
text typeface—Garamond (11 on 13);
text paper—60 pound Warrens "1854";
endpapers—Multicolor Antique, Cafe;
cover (on .088 boards)—Holliston Roxite C (56662);
and jacket—Permacote Offset, linen finish,
printed two colors (PMS 547C, Blue, and PMS 465C, Beige),
and varnished.

Printing (offset lithography) and binding were by
Braun-Brumfield, Inc., Ann Arbor, Michigan.